Doublefields

Doublefields

Memories and Stories

by Elizabeth Enright

Harcourt, Brace & World, Inc.
New York

First edition

Library of Congress Catalog Card Number: 66-23806

Printed in the United States of America

The following stories appeared originally in *The New Yorker:* "The Shush Rush," "A Green Shade," "The Caterpillar Summer," "Dragons, Policemen and Early Morning Screams," and "The Sandals of Monsieur de Flandre." Others appeared originally in *Cosmopolitan, Ladies' Home Journal, Mademoiselle, Redbook, University of Kansas City Review,* and *Yale Review.*

For Robin Gillham

Contents

Contents

Memories

The Walnut Shell

When I woke in my crib in the earliest mornings of my life, the city was always awake before me. I remember how it jostled and rumbled and jolted and clanged as if morning came trotting in a huge loose harness. The horses I could hear were trotting like that, with a heavy brisk clopping; and the wheels of the drays they pulled clattered and banged and rang the loose manhole lids down in the street. Whistles were blowing, and horns were blowing, and when it was windy a sign that I never saw creaked and squeaked on an iron standard, to and fro, to and fro. Sometimes there was a noise of bells; they did not chime or peal, but had more of a metal rattle, and then an early bird went croaking: "Paycack Ko! Paycack Ko!" I could not see him, but in my mind's eye he was mean and small, a hunchback dressed in black, who squawked this useless chant without a reason. It was years before I knew that he was calling: "Pay cash, clothes! Pay cash, clothes!" and that the blunted tonk of bells I heard came from his peddler's cart. Sometimes, even so early, there was the dreadful surprise of a hurdy-gurdy. Abrupt, hysterical, the rendition of "Ciribiribin" or "La Paloma" burst out with a racket of laughter and doorbells. I hated the hurdy-gurdys, and even my change-resentful soul refused to mourn when years later they were silenced.

I would lie waiting for my parents to wake up, waiting for the moment when the window would be closed, the shade would leap up and snap against the roller, and I was liberated from my crib.

My father was cheerful in the mornings; as he stropped his razor in the bathroom he sang a song called "Anybody Here Seen Kelly?" Most mornings from the time I was two till the time I was six I watched him shave, or looked in on him while he was shaving, and often when he had a good big beard of lather on he'd come toward me pretending he was going to give me a kiss, and I would take off squealing down the hall to the kitchen, where Frances Moynihan was cooking bacon.

Shortly before the First World War my parents, young artists, moved to New York from the Middle West to seek their fortunes, bringing me with them, a baby of one year.

They also brought their talents, which were considerable, and very little money. It was necessary to find an apartment that did not cost much, and to their surprise they did find one quite easily; a very nice one, far uptown in the hundred-and-forties on the corner of Broadway.

The apartment house was a ten-story building, for some reason called the Woodmere. It had a broad green glass visor over one entrance, tipped up and peaked in the middle like the snout of a monstrous turtle. I cannot remember the lobby or the elevators, but I remember that entrance very well, and best of all I remember our apartment on the ninth floor.

There were six rooms: a large airy living room, a smaller one adjoining it that was my mother's studio, a dining room, two bedrooms, two bathrooms, a big sunny kitchen, and a long dark hall that gleamed with floor polish. For this my father paid eighty-five dollars a month.

Memory insists on large dimensions and confronted with fact is often proved a liar; but my parents both assure me that our apartment really *was* a spacious one, and we cannot all be wrong. Certainly it seemed immense to me.

Our front windows looked out over rooftops and many chimney smokes to the Hudson River and beyond it to the Palisades. There was a lot of sky above, a huge amount of sky that nothing ever interrupted except birds. All the other windows looked south over miles of city: more rooftops, more chimney smokes, and the pigtailed buses crawling on Riverside Drive.

We had sun the whole day long and plenty of room; we had vast garish spreads of sunset, and a fine array of spangles after dark. My father and mother were pleased with what they had found and wondered that it had been so easy.

They soon had a clue when I was overtaken by some childhood ailment. Knowing no doctor in the city, my mother called the office of Emmet Holt, the Dr. Spock of his day, whose book she knew by heart. Dr. Holt was out of town; his assistant Dr. Frederic Bartlett came instead.

The maid let him in, my mother being busy with me, but a moment later when she hurried into the living room she found the doctor peering through his glasses at the signature on an Utamaro print. He turned, looked at her rather severely, and said: "*This* is a very extraordinary apartment to find in such a neighborhood."

That was the first hint she had that we were living on what

some people might consider the wrong side of the tracks. This did not bother her at all; I think she was pleased.

Both my parents worked hard. They had to. My father rented a studio downtown in the Flatiron Building to which he went each morning like a regular business father, but my mother worked at home in *her* studio. It was closed away by two pairs of glass doors: one leading to the living room, one to the hall. Before I was old enough to go to kindergarten I often used to stand outside the ones at the end of the hall and watch my mother at work, a figure totally concentrated. Her drawing board was tilted against a large table, and on a smaller one beside her was a litter of paint dishes, water bowls, wrecked and twisted Windsor, Newton tubes. If she was painting, there would be paint stripes on her face; if she was drawing, there would be pencil dust and swipes of Higgins Ink. Brushes and pencils were thrust at random into her dark top-knot so that she had the appearance of a disturbed geisha. Sometimes she whistled as she worked; sometimes she held the board away from her and looked at it, head first on one side, then on the other, the way a bird looks at things. When she sharpened her pencil she used a penknife, like a boy whittling a twig.

I learned early that my whines and snuffles were in vain, that I could not go in that room when she was working: the work was serious; it was to earn money. I had my toys, the company of whoever was in the kitchen, my rides in the go-cart, the run of the rest of the apartment.

Often I went into the living room. It was always bright with river light and sky. There was an Oriental rug on the floor, rose-brown and azure blue. And the couch under the south windows was covered with blue and studded with hard buttons. Sometimes I climbed up on it and sat there, the morning sunshine baking my neck. Flanking the couch were two tall bookcases that had been designed by my uncle the architect and that looked as if they were wearing burglar's caps; and near the entrance to the dining room (more glass doors) stood my father's Morris chair. In my memory I smell that chair: a smell of horse; and I remember that the rattan strips wrapped around the arms were brittle and could be peeled or broken off in bits when nobody was looking.

On the walls the sneering ladies of Japan, tilted on clogs, stared obliquely from their pillar prints, and above the piano Nichiren, exiled in Sado, toiled up a snowy slope forever, his straw disk hat butted against the wind.

The piano was a Steinway that it took my mother three years to pay for: a pedigreed animal, black as licorice and white as teeth. On the sounding board just between the string-pegs and the music rack, within a wreath of royal crests, was the name of the makers: "Steinway & Son. London. New York. Hamburg." Sometimes even now I lift the lid and read the names of all those majesties to whom the makers were appointed: William II, German Emperor and King of Prussia; Nicholas II, Czar of Russia; Alfonso XIII, King of Spain; Franz Joseph I, Emperor of Austria and King of Hungary; Oscar II, King of Sweden; Edward VII, King of Great Britain and Emperor of India; Umberto I, King of Italy; Albert, King of Saxony; Mohammed Ali, Shah of Persia; Abdul-Hamid II, Sultan of Turkey (many so soon to be upset, deposed, exiled, or brought to ruin, and all finally to be dead, so soon).

Every now and then my mother would burst from her studio, streaked like an Ojibway, to drop down at the piano and rest herself with music. She played well, with flair and vigor. Off she would go, flying, on Rupert Henselt's "If I Were a Bird," or Chopin's Butterfly Etude, or one of the mazurkas. Sometimes I would crawl under the piano while she played, and then I had a house with a roof of music. I liked to sit there and let the thunder of it jar my teeth and shake my bones.

In many ways it was a fine thing to have parents who were artists. When I tried to draw a beautiful mermaid I had great trouble with her hair. It came out square every time, like the roof and walls of a shed; I couldn't make it bend around her head and ripple the way I wanted it.

"You do it for me, Mother," I would say, and she, with a few strokes of her pencil, would give the mermaid a wealth of waving tresses that reached to the tip of her tail.

When my cloth doll's face grew boring or was damaged I took her to my father, and he would paint her a new one with his oil paints (blue eyes or brown, as directed, dimples, two pearly teeth) and hang her up to dry. That was Mary Louise, my favorite, who could not be forced into beauty no matter how many faces were given her; her head was the wrong shape, wide at the ears like a football, and she was idiotically pigeon-toed. Still, I liked her; she had a kindly smell. My other doll, Sister Mandy, I never liked. It did not occur to me to give her away or throw her away; I thought I was stuck with her the way one would be stuck with a sister or brother. She had a snub nose, wide blue eyes, a tight little mouth, and a boy's haircut. What I sensed in her, I see now, was a sort of humorless assurance; she was no fun, or would not have been if she had been a person. My Teddy bear was a good old thing. I cut him a little bald spot for the top of his head to match my father's.

There were two other dolls in the house, but they were family dolls and lived in the dining room on a broad shelf above the window. I spent a lot of time in that room because in those days I did not care for eating; and the word "permissive" not having yet been uttered, I was made to stay until I *ate*. I remember the extreme tedium of my high chair; of being fenced in by a tray on which the task before me—the bowl of oatmeal or the monstrous potato—was odious. Some comfort was to be derived from the dolls, two kachinas, which my father had got in Oraibi when, as a very young man, he had lived for several months among the Hopis. One of the dolls had a square ferocious mask, the other a bland triangular smile. I did not trust her (I was sure it was a she), but I liked the square one, who was named Itchikabooboo. Both had tufts of chicken feathers on their heads, and I believed that they were secretly alive.

Such fancies for some reason were thought desirable, and were encouraged in me. It is a wonder to me that I ever grew up with any sense of reality, or even with any *sense*. Until I was eight years old I believed in fairies just as truly as I believed in dogs and cats. I believed that there was a fairy whose particular concern was the collecting of my teeth, that kobolds lived in chimneys, that magic was a fact, and that my mother had it in her to become a witch.

There was a reason for the last. My parents had the complete assurance of people to whom the phrase "child psychology" is the phrase of faddists. They used their own methods with perfect confidence. When I was bad my mother, on occasion, would simply threaten to "turn into a wicked witch." She had a terrible face that she could make and that brought me groveling to rectitude at once. My father could become a giant. All *he* had to do was to say: "Fee-Fi-Fo-Fum!" (To do them justice, they did not use these methods often.)

When I wanted to frighten myself, as I sometimes did, all I had to do was to take from my bookcase a volume of fairy tales illustrated by Edmund Dulac, in which one picture of the Beast, in "Beauty and the Beast," was the most blood-chilling image of horror my mind could imagine. One look was enough; icy with the fear I craved I'd push the book back and run for my life.

My diet was fairy tales. I wanted to hear nothing but stories of princes who turned into foxes, and wicked stepmothers who, for punishment, were made to dance in red-hot iron shoes till they fell dead. Imbued with thoughts of privilege and crowns, I loved the word "Palisades" because I thought it was "palace-ades."

Every night when I was in bed my father would sit beside my crib and tell me a story of his own. Another fairy tale, of course. Sometimes he was smoking a cigar; and that orange eye that glowed and faded was the one light in the room, and the smoke was cozy.

"Once upon a time there was a little girl who lived on the edge of the world in a walnut shell that rocked and rocked when the wind blew; and one day—"

That was how one of his stories began. There were many others: The Pumpkin-Pie Princess, The Road That Stopped in the Middle, The Journey to the Colored Stars. When I was very young he used to sing me a song he had learned in the Indian country; a softly booming chant that he said was a lullaby. It sounded like frogs to me.

Sometimes I woke in the depths of the night for a little while. Wind came into the bedroom through the large open window; the curtains flitted at the sides; and beyond, in the brownish, city-colored night, there were chains of light along the drive; above them, a little to the left, and south, the Clare-mont Restaurant crowned its knoll, oval-shaped, a cake of lights, more alluring in its suggestion of magical festivity, of magical reward, than anything I ever saw again. I watched it and thought about it and longed to visit it for myself.

Once I tried this. I was three, or perhaps four, and having wakened sometime in the night I looked out at the sparkling oval and knew that the time had come to make the journey. Some nights before, my parents (fast asleep now) had brought me a hat from a party they had gone to. It was made of card-board, tall and cone-shaped, covered with glazed green paper and trimmed with frizzled pompons and a silver ribbon. It was perched on one of the foot posts of my crib, and now I plucked it off and put it on my head, since it was obviously the right thing to wear on such a trip. I did not bother with a bathrobe; my nightgown seemed appropriate enough.

I had to be careful climbing over the lowered crib rail. It was made of painted iron and capable of a grating squawk if one put any weight on it. My bare feet made no sound on the floor of the bedroom, or of the long hall that led to the front door. The hall was very dark but I felt no fear. I remember exactly how I felt: perfectly sure that I would overcome all obstacles—if in fact I should meet any—and come soon to that place where there would be—everything I wanted, I suppose, and things even better than the ones I wanted.

But the front door was where I came a cropper. The chain bolt was on, and my efforts to unfasten it caused a clatter.

The hall light snapped on; my mother came running to me.

"Elizabeth, what are you *doing?* Where are you *going?*"

"To the Claremont," I answered reasonably.

"Oh, no! No, you're not, darling. Back to sleep, that's where *you're* going!" My mother picked me up in her arms and carried me back to bed. "Where do you think she was going, Pat?" she said to my father as she tucked me in. When she told him, they both looked down at me, laughing indulgently from their high grown-up place.

Was I glad to be rescued from my journey? I wonder. I don't remember. But I did not set out on it again; I knew now that I would never reach my goal, as perhaps, deep down, I had known all along.

For most of our years in the Woodmere, Frances Moynihan was our cook, maid, housekeeper, and laundress. When I had no governess or what would now be called a "sitter," she did my governing and sitting. Before she came I had had a German nurse named Ilse, with cheeks like eggplants and no eyelashes. She was supposed to take me to St. Nicholas Park in the afternoons, but she often took me to more interesting places.

Once I went with her to the dentist, and because we were early for her appointment we sat facing the dentist's chair and watched a woman have her tooth pulled, watched and listened as the poor creature howled and warbled. When the dentist, sweating, finally yanked the tooth out, he waved it at us in his forceps to give us a good look, then popped it under a tumbler on the dental tray as if he feared it might run away on the little legs it seemed to have.

Once she took me downtown on the streetcar, far downtown, where we went into a building and up some stairs to a sort of classroom where there were a lot of people. A fat man with a yellow fishtail mustache was drawing airplanes on a blackboard, and everyone spoke German.

Once she took me to the movies, where I had never been before, and from which I was led screaming. On the screen an old lady had leaned over to pluck the sunbonnet from a creeping child, but I was sure she had plucked off its head.

My life with Ilse was eventful but it was brief, and then there was always Frances.

She was a short elderly woman, with thin hair coiled into a little snail on top of her head. Her cheeks were pleated, her eyes tiny, black as crickets in her yellowing face. She had no shape; she was a squat wide bundle with no lap to sit on, only a short slope. Her shoes had slits cut into them for comfort, and she was cross all the time. She had a grown daughter named *Add*-ele, and a big pocketbook she called a "satchel."

"Yeh?" was her response to any news I brought her, and "Too bad about you" was her response to any complaint. Yet she made me a beautiful quilt for my dolls' bed, and when my father and mother went out for the evening she read me fairy tales after supper. We sat in the kitchen then. I remember the black window and the shuddering lights of the city, the ticking of the kitchen clock, the wind at the coping, and the flat, flat, dogged voice: " 'So he sent a messenger to the other bride, and begged her to go home, as he already had a wife, and he who has an old dish does not need a new one. Their marriage was then celebrated, and the Lion was taken into favor again,' and that's all, so go on with you, go on to bed now, go on."

"You come with me then."

"What's the matter? Scared? A big girl like you?"

Yes, I was scared. The Beast was in the bedroom bookcase.

"Too bad about you!" But she would come and scold me out of my clothes and into bed, tuck the covers under the mattress with vigorous jolts, as if her own kindness exasperated her.

"I'll be right in the kitchen but don't be calling, now!"

And soon I would be calling: *"Fran-ces!"*

"Now, what! You lay down and go to sleep. I never saw such a young one!"

Then she would sit in the room until I slept.

Sometimes she took me to call on her best friend, Mrs. Buckley. (Though they had known each other many years they called each other Mrs.) Mrs. Buckley had a dark dense little parlor that smelled of fried potatoes. The two stout women, two mounds, sat drinking tea and talking, while I sat on a plush-covered hassock that stung and tried to make friends with the cat. It was so old its fur was stubbed off, and it was deaf besides: one of those white, afflicted cats. I do not think I have ever known a boredom to surpass the boredom of those visits.

One day when we came back to the Woodmere, Frances found she had not brought the key to the apartment. We were locked out and nobody was home.

"I know what I'm going to do," she said, and rang the doorbell of a neighbor across the hall. When the woman opened the door, Frances asked if she might use her kitchen window.

"Window?" The woman stared.

"I got to get back to my kitchen. Got to get the roast in. We're locked out."

Just below the windows of the ninth floor there was a sort of coping, or shelf, with a moat, or gutter, in it to catch the water from the eaves above, I suppose.

"You're not going to crawl along *that* thing, are you?" demanded the neighbor, appalled.

"The only way, and I got to hustle," Frances said. "Now you mind the lady!" she ordered me severely. Then she raised the sash, straddled the sill, and settled on the coping on her hands and knees. I have never forgotten the rear view of Frances crawling along that shelf: her hat with its sideways ornament of wired ribbon and famished plume; her work skirt with the placket-split; the creeping soles of her old shoes. The shelf was hardly more than two feet wide, the street nine stories down. The neighbor woman, her children, and I, all leaned from the kitchen window, watching the brave creature creep to the corner of the building and tack around it out of sight; then we hurried to the hall and waited. When we heard footsteps in our apartment the neighbor woman let out a great sigh. Frances flung open the door, and her black eyes were blazing. Triumph crackled all around her.

Oh, life was exciting in those days! Everything else has been tame by comparison. My first six years in the world were shot through with as many colors and glitters as the first circus I ever saw, which in my memory went on all day and night like a Chinese theater, dreadful with clowns exploding from cannons, blinding with jewels and the smell of beasts.

Besides the circus, there was the opera they took me to, where Hänsel and Gretel, each bosomed like a cook, did a dance in wooden shoes, angels came down from heaven on a golden escalator, and the drum in the orchestra was worse than the clown-cannon.

There was Nijinsky, all in pink, with a helmet of petals: the Specter of the Rose. I pretend that I remember his leap through the window, but what I really remember is his figure poised at the footlights, the great drumstick muscles of his thighs, the arms curved above his head, and the face tilted downward, pensive and lonely: an ethereal football player.

There was Pavlova, who, scarcely touching the surface of the stage, glided across it with a quivering perfection that was like nothing so much as the exquisite vibration of the wings of certain moths. Pavlova was my first goddess; I saw her many times, and when I was older, through anguished practice and determination, I was able to rise to my *pointes* wearing sneakers.

Sometime during those years I was taken to the Horace Mann kindergarten: an enormous place with pans of bean sprouts on the window sills, blocks on the shelves, and, grouped in a corner, an assemblage of large, blotched dolls that looked as if they were suffering from hives. Our teacher, Miss Garrison, knew everything and had a very beautiful accordion-pleated green petticoat that showed when she did the goose step. Her assistant, Miss Brown, wore a lavender dress and had cool round arms the color of milk. She was the one who told us not to eat the paste, which it had never occurred to us to do, but which from then on we ate.

Among the friends I made I remember the girl who wore two ribbon rosettes at her temples like a pony at a fair, the girl who always wore white, even white shoes, and the dark-eyed boy who was part Cherokee Indian, and who caused the name "Oliver" to be beautiful to my ears ever afterward. And of the succession of women who called for me at noon I remember Mrs. Gorselin, who resembled the Statue of Liberty and whom I loathed and hated (vicious hatred was by no means unknown to me), and the Southern one with a voice like fog; the pretty one who yawned all the time, and, best of the lot, Goody, Miss McGoodwin, who came and stayed with us for years. She was tall, with large, pale eyes, and when she took the pins from her hair it fell in a lank, dense cape to her knees. Sometimes she let me brush it for her.

"It ain't healthy," Frances used to say. "Strength's all gone to her hair." And perhaps she was right. Goody died of tuberculosis before she was thirty-five.

But that was long after we left the Woodmere. In the meantime life went on its exhilarating way and nothing was sad. At night there was the fairy tale and the cigar light, in the daytime there was kindergarten, where there were interesting things to do like weaving mats and eating paste; there was the park, which seemed to be a different place each afternoon, and the coming home to a dashing sound of piano music, or of several people talking and laughing in the living room, for my parents were young, and when the workday was over they wanted to have fun.

Sometimes, very often, a moment all intact comes before my thoughts. It is an early evening in winter. The lamps are not yet lighted. My mother and two other women, finished with their tea, are sitting in the dusk beside the littered tea tray. I watch, and listen to them talk. Lights travel the river, travel the street; sometimes they brush more and softer lights across the ceiling. One of the women wears a sweeping hat. I see her as I saw her then: aquiline profile, dark eyebrow, earring made of pearls. Her hair is gray but she is young.

Nobody can tell me her name, but how many hundred times, I wonder, for what reason I can never guess, have my thoughts returned that face to me, and with it the sight of the dim room, the lights brushing the ceiling, and the sound of women's voices talking quietly because of the dusk. A moment lives again, and will again, and will forever, or at least as long as I do.

As for the apartment itself, it not only refuses to be forgotten, but also has continued all my life to impose itself, in bizarre ways, as a setting. Often I realize this when I am reading. When I read *Pride and Prejudice*, for example, where was it that Elizabeth Bennet joyfully caused Fitzwilliam Darcy to account for his having fallen in love with her? It was in the living room of that apartment, green English countryside beyond the windows notwithstanding. When I read *War and Peace*, where was it that the Rostovs and their guests assembled for the glorious party given to celebrate the name day of the Countess and her young daughter, Natasha? It was in our apartment on the ninth floor of the Woodmere at Broadway and a Hundred and Forty-first Street: servants in livery, ikons and riches added, but unmistakably our apartment—that place of large light rooms which, for one human being, set a lifetime pattern for all happy backgrounds.

How could I know, when I lived there, that we would leave the Woodmere for good before I was seven? Or that my father would go away to war, and that after that my parents would separate and find other partners, and life would go on changing and changing forever? All I know is that once it did seem settled. Once I lived in what seemed a permanent place: a kingdom full of colors that was ruled by Grownups.

Grownups! Everyone remembers them. How strange and even sad it is that we never became what they were: beings noble, infallible, and free. We never became *them*. One of the things we discover as we live is that we never become anything different from what we are. We are no less ourselves at forty than we were at four, and because of this we know grownups as Grownups only once in life: during our own childhood. We never meet them in our lives again, and we will miss them always.

The Shush Rush

When we were eight years old Ira Glackens and I organized, publicized, and performed the major roles in a colorful outdoor ceremony, the purpose of which was to unite us in the bond of brother and sister. The ritual, which combined the best features of both the baptismal and marriage services, took place at a drinking fountain in the northeast corner of Washington Square. That, at least, was where it first took place. I wore a veil which was unusually long since it was made of a let-out ballet skirt, and we exchanged rings which were circles of wire strung with big blue, white, and yellow beads that felt like lumps of crockery on the hand. Time and determination had gone into the undertaking; it was not like those other projects which were known to be doomed even in the moment of design: the plan to harness together fifty toy gas balloons, suspend a small chair from them, and take turns flying slowly over the park, or the plan to outwit the guards at the Metropolitan Museum and spend the night in the Egyptian room among the sarcophagi and dog-faced goddesses. No, this was one project that was thought out, prepared for, and actually accomplished.

The event was well attended by persons under four feet tall, some on roller skates, some leaning casually on hoops or scooter handles, one or two on tricycles, and it was so success- ful that it had to be repeated at every drinking fountain in the square.

I took my place beside Ira, nervously glancing over my shoulder at the sweeping soiled expanse of train behind me; in front of us stood the minister, a member of the audience or congregation who had been pressed into service and vigorously briefed beforehand.

"Shut up, everybody, we're going to begin," ordered Ira. "Go on, start."

"All right. Well, do you, Elizabeth, take this boy, Ira, to be your lawful brother?" asked the minister, snickering.

"Yes, I do," I said, snickering, too, and stuffing one of my long lank curls into my mouth to keep from laughing louder.

"And do you, Ira, take this girl, Elizabeth, to be your lawful sister?"

"I do," Ira conceded. "Quit giggling or we'll get somebody else."

"Which comes next, I forget, the water or the rings?" the minister wanted to know.

"The water, the water!" clamored the congregation.

"Silly, the rings come next," Ira said. "The water's last, it *seals it*."

So we exchanged our rings which were too big but could be twisted to fit, and then after more questions and responses, now forgotten, the minister handed his Bible—a volume of

Though not supposed to cross the avenue alone we often did so, to explore the western section where the old Italian men in their dark coats stood together—never sat—in cackling contentious groups like grackles on a newly seeded lawn. Out of their pockets their folded newspapers glared with big black foreign words. We, on our skates, swooped around them, in and out of their flooding language that poured and babbled with a sound of passion and outrage. It was always surprising to hear them laugh and know that that fierce tongue could be used for telling jokes.

On the benches sat their wives and daughters, cracking pistachio nuts and littering the ground with dyed red shells. There was a hearty voluble atmosphere about that region of the park, a lot of eating and arguing were going on, babies bawled and were comforted by breast or bottle, the old women offered council in hoarse, used voices, or laughed, showing violet gums and token teeth; the old men ranted and deplored. Above it all Alexander Lyman Holley looked out with benevolent bronze eyes, and across the avenue Garibaldi in his pillbox hat and little cape gazed toward his countrymen and drew his sword perpetually above the squabbling of children.

We liked our park, although we recognized that it was poor in possibilities compared to others. Central Park was almost like real country with lakes, forests, cliffs, and all enormous. Gramercy Park was small but clean and pretty, and only people with keys to the gate could play behind its metal bars, like high-class birds in an aviary. But our park was neither wilderness nor sanctuary. There were more trees than now—horse chestnuts, and many plane trees dotted with seedballs and grimed sparrows—but still not enough to make a forest or even woods. There was nothing much to explore. When we climbed between the iron fence rungs looking for jungles and anxious for treasure, we found only dull shrubbery and

the Little Colonel series—to a bystander, dipped his hands into the drinking fountain, and drew cold dripping crosses on our foreheads.

"There," said Ira over his shoulder as he strolled away. "Now we're brother and sister. We'll have the next service pretty soon down by Garibaldi."

I tore off my veil, put my ring in my pocket and joined gladly in a game of squat tag with the Ryan girls.

It is no wonder that Ira was the brother of my choice. When he entered the park, thin and spectacled, drama came with him. He was never one of the crude battle-organizers on skates, nor was he content to whang at pebbles with a hockey stick, or spend his ingenuity on marbles. Instead he could tell a ghost story that would turn your bones to jelly. He could impersonate characters of extreme malevolence, paint witch masks, and compose insulting poetry. He had a toy theater with real lights, a handsome collection of Niagara coal, and many disguises with beards. He knew all the names of the Egyptian deities and left offerings of Nabisco wafers at Per Neb's tomb whenever he went to the museum. He was the founder of one secret society after another, all short-lived: inception, not continuity, interested him. For a few days, dazzled as mullet by a light, we followed his strict diagrams for ritual, never forgetting the eccentric handclasp, the secret word, the long level glance between members. As soon as he lost interest in it the sinister etiquette would be abandoned; we could not keep it up without him. But no one mourned; we knew that soon there would be something else to take its place.

He and many of the rest of us were the children of artists. We were used to the sight of fond faces streaked with cobalt or rose madder. The air of home was spiced with turpentine or the flat dense smell of Higgins Ink, and we were accustomed to tiptoeing past the particular closed door behind which could be heard the mild scraping of a palette knife, or the ting-a-ling of the water-color brush as it dipped into the glass. When we were at our play outdoors we knew that we had left behind one parent at least who was dabbing and dotting at a picture, backing away from the easel into the furniture, or holding the drawing board up to a mirror, the long brush gripped between the teeth, and the eyes fierce with scrutiny.

We were infected by our atmosphere. We ourselves were more often paint-streaked than other children. We drew pictures on the broad park pavement and all of us had our specialties. Mine was beautiful women with crowded, fleecy Mary Pickford curls; Ira drew mummies, of course; and there was one child who made the same picture over and over again: the profile of a girl with her eyes shut. Printed beneath it were the words: "Anne closed her eyes to shut out the awful sight."

"What sight? What awful sight, Shirley?" we begged. But she would never tell us; she smiled dreamily and shook her head. "Too awful. Too horrible. It wouldn't be good for you to know."

For our pavement drawings we used French chalk which we bought at Bigelow's drugstore in flat slabs. It was smooth and cool and dry and did not rub off on clothes and black ribbed stockings like the regular chalk that came in boxes, sweetly colored as Necco candy. I can remember exactly how it felt to be drawing on the pavement, allowed neither to kneel nor sit, but crouched over, snuffling monotonously, chewing the knotted, exhausted elastic that was supposed to keep my hat on my head, and all my long hair swinging and getting in the way. Oh, the tediums and discomforts that attend the play of children which are recognized only when the play is over!

Sometimes we drew other kinds of things, arrows for hare and hounds, dots for the game of boxes, the two designs for

hopscotch: one straight like a ladder, one curled up like a shell. I can still hear the skate key ringing onto the pa missing or making the point. I can still remember the e ment of the first spring jump-rope days; breathlessly le the live arc like a ballerina between the two who ground chanted. There were always incantations in the spring for the jump rope, one for ball-bouncing, one for jacks for the tranced group watching the moving finger o counter-out: "Ibbetty bibbetty sibbetty sab, ibbetty bib kinahba. My . . . Mother . . . Says . . . To . . . Ch . . . You."

The incantations and the games are much the same t but what has happened to the playthings? Where are the wheel roller skates, so much lighter and faster than the wheel kind? Where is the hockey stick that did more to b shins than any other single factor, and the great wha wooden hoops bowling and glittering in the afternoon shine? Where is the Diabolo spool, and the little blown hopping in its cup of wire? One's childhood never seem mote until such things are considered, and then one finds one is the product of a dead era: the age of the buttonhook the pantywaist and the Indian penny. . . .

In those days there were more nurses in the Square now. Stout, wrapped against the weather, they sat on benches in rows, the perambulators rocking in front of t like boats tied up to docks. They had their own life toget gossiping and discussing and laughing a lot. Occasionally among them would rise, scanning distances, and a great cr name or a command, would come ringing from her. To us t were part of the scene, not of the action. They were buttressed background of authority and, only if necessary refuge. For the most part we kept away from them, pursu our ruthless independent ways as far as possible from range of comment.

parched grass full of chewing-gum papers. The angry park man was our only tiger, and burnt black carbon sticks from the arc lamps were as near as we could come to treasure: they made pretty good chalk. But we were not discouraged that all our sapphires turned out to be pieces of magnesia bottle and all our silver crumbs of tin foil. We continued to search. And children are more fortunate, or perhaps less cordial to disappointment than adults: where no treasure exists for their discovery they will invent it, or add the concept of value to something hitherto unclaimed. It is their necessity not so much to find what they are seeking, as to find the thing to seek.

The sour park earth was earth after all; real worms lived in it, real roots confined it, and real stones were dredged up by time to its sooty surface. Our eyes were caught at last by a glitter that had possibilities: small pieces of rock, full of mica flakes. Ira took one in his hand; it was soft and he crumbled it. On his palm the particles were separate and shimmering, a powder of gold. The importance of the fact struck us at the same moment.

"This stuff is valuable," Ira said tensely. "Listen, we can grind this stuff up and make gold dust out of it. Find some more, go on, hurry up, and then we'll take it somewhere secret and experiment. I'll find some, too, and listen! Don't let anyone know! Don't let them see and don't explain."

Close-lipped, secretive, I searched the dingy grass for mica stones and found a pocketful. Ira did too. We met and made our way to the side of one of the shrubbery triangles somewhat out of the main stream of activity; there was no true seclusion in that park.

Stamping on the stones was unsuccessful. Ira found two larger, harder rocks and we squatted on our haunches—obedient to the last, we did not sit—and pounded stubbornly like Navajo squaws preparing meal. The soft stones crumbled and crushed, becoming a glittering powder; some silver, some gold. Our industry and noise attracted attention, everybody came and asked us what we were doing.

"Go away," we said. "We are busy."

Nobody thought of going. More came. Even the girl we hated because her hair was clipped close like a boy's. Ira said she had leprosy and to keep out of her breathing range. Her upper lip was always chapped and we further despised her because not only did she not know she was an outcast but she believed herself to be a leader.

"What are you doing?" she asked, and when we didn't answer she kept it up. "Hm? What are you doing? Hm? I said what are you—"

"We're making an explosive. We're the only ones that know how to handle it," Ira said. "It's so deadly that even its name is deadly. We don't dare to say it, we have to call it Shush."

"Oh, you do not," she said, but edged away a little on her skates, and we kept on pounding.

"Shush is a good name," I said.

"I know it," said Ira.

Our friends now wished to take part in our enterprise but we were not ready to let them. On that first day it had not yet occurred to them that stones exactly like these could be collected by anyone. We still had priority, and the piles of glistening powder grew. We were clumsy then, we hurt ourselves and wasted material, but we soon became skillful.

For we were diligent. Each afternoon we set out like laborers, armed with hammers, potato mashers, pillboxes, mason jars, or other receptacles. We spent hours squatting and pounding, gathering up crumbs between chapped fingers. We became expert and selective: the Shush was assayed and graded, that with too much dirt in it being thrown away or offered to the innocent. We traded in pinches, and used it for barter; we hoarded and gloated, for as the Shush became currency the Little Colonel series—to a bystander, dipped his hands into the drinking fountain, and drew cold dripping crosses on our foreheads.

"There," said Ira over his shoulder as he strolled away. "Now we're brother and sister. We'll have the next service pretty soon down by Garibaldi."

I tore off my veil, put my ring in my pocket and joined gladly in a game of squat tag with the Ryan girls.

It is no wonder that Ira was the brother of my choice. When he entered the park, thin and spectacled, drama came with him. He was never one of the crude battle-organizers on skates, nor was he content to whang at pebbles with a hockey stick, or spend his ingenuity on marbles. Instead he could tell a ghost story that would turn your bones to jelly. He could impersonate characters of extreme malevolence, paint witch masks, and compose insulting poetry. He had a toy theater with real lights, a handsome collection of Niagara coal, and many disguises with beards. He knew all the names of the Egyptian deities and left offerings of Nabisco wafers at Per Neb's tomb whenever he went to the museum. He was the founder of one secret society after another, all short-lived: inception, not continuity, interested him. For a few days, dazzled as mullet by a light, we followed his strict diagrams for ritual, never forgetting the eccentric handclasp, the secret word, the long level glance between members. As soon as he lost interest in it the sinister etiquette would be abandoned; we could not keep it up without him. But no one mourned; we knew that soon there would be something else to take its place.

He and many of the rest of us were the children of artists. We were used to the sight of fond faces streaked with cobalt or rose madder. The air of home was spiced with turpentine or the flat dense smell of Higgins Ink, and we were accustomed to tiptoeing past the particular closed door behind which could be heard the mild scraping of a palette knife, or the ting-a-ling of the water-color brush as it dipped into the glass. When we were at our play outdoors we knew that we had left behind one parent at least who was dabbing and dotting at a picture, backing away from the easel into the furniture, or holding the drawing board up to a mirror, the long brush gripped between the teeth, and the eyes fierce with scrutiny.

We were infected by our atmosphere. We ourselves were more often paint-streaked than other children. We drew pictures on the broad park pavement and all of us had our specialties. Mine was beautiful women with crowded, fleecy Mary Pickford curls; Ira drew mummies, of course; and there was one child who made the same picture over and over again: the profile of a girl with her eyes shut. Printed beneath it were the words: "Anne closed her eyes to shut out the awful sight."

"What sight? What awful sight, Shirley?" we begged. But she would never tell us; she smiled dreamily and shook her head. "Too awful. Too horrible. It wouldn't be good for you to know."

For our pavement drawings we used French chalk which we bought at Bigelow's drugstore in flat slabs. It was smooth and cool and dry and did not rub off on clothes and black ribbed stockings like the regular chalk that came in boxes, sweetly colored as Necco candy. I can remember exactly how it felt to be drawing on the pavement, allowed neither to kneel nor sit, but crouched over, snuffling monotonously, chewing the knotted, exhausted elastic that was supposed to keep my hat on my head, and all my long hair swinging and getting in the way. Oh, the tediums and discomforts that attend the play of children which are recognized only when the play is over!

Sometimes we drew other kinds of things, arrows for hare and hounds, dots for the game of boxes, the two designs for hopscotch: one straight like a ladder, one curled up like a snail shell. I can still hear the skate key ringing onto the pattern, missing or making the point. I can still remember the excitement of the first spring jump-rope days; breathlessly leaping the live arc like a ballerina between the two who ground and chanted. There were always incantations in the spring; one for the jump rope, one for ball-bouncing, one for jacks, one for the tranced group watching the moving finger of the counter-out: "Ibbetty bibbetty sibbetty sab, ibbetty bibbetty kinahba. My . . . Mother . . . Says . . . To . . . Choose . . . You."

The incantations and the games are much the same today, but what has happened to the playthings? Where are the two-wheel roller skates, so much lighter and faster than the four-wheel kind? Where is the hockey stick that did more to bruise shins than any other single factor, and the great whacked wooden hoops bowling and glittering in the afternoon sunshine? Where is the Diabolo spool, and the little blown ball hopping in its cup of wire? One's childhood never seems remote until such things are considered, and then one finds that one is the product of a dead era: the age of the buttonhook and the pantywaist and the Indian penny. . . .

In those days there were more nurses in the Square than now. Stout, wrapped against the weather, they sat on the benches in rows, the perambulators rocking in front of them like boats tied up to docks. They had their own life together, gossiping and discussing and laughing a lot. Occasionally one among them would rise, scanning distances, and a great cry, a name or a command, would come ringing from her. To us they were part of the scene, not of the action. They were the buttressed background of authority and, only if necessary, of refuge. For the most part we kept away from them, pursuing our ruthless independent ways as far as possible from the range of comment.

Though not supposed to cross the avenue alone we often did so, to explore the western section where the old Italian men in their dark coats stood together—never sat—in cackling contentious groups like grackles on a newly seeded lawn. Out of their pockets their folded newspapers glared with big black foreign words. We, on our skates, swooped around them, in and out of their flooding language that poured and babbled with a sound of passion and outrage. It was always surprising to hear them laugh and know that that fierce tongue could be used for telling jokes.

On the benches sat their wives and daughters, cracking pistachio nuts and littering the ground with dyed red shells. There was a hearty voluble atmosphere about that region of the park, a lot of eating and arguing were going on, babies bawled and were comforted by breast or bottle, the old women offered council in hoarse, used voices, or laughed, showing violet gums and token teeth; the old men ranted and deplored. Above it all Alexander Lyman Holley looked out with benevolent bronze eyes, and across the avenue Garibaldi in his pillbox hat and little cape gazed toward his countrymen and drew his sword perpetually above the squabbling of children.

We liked our park, although we recognized that it was poor in possibilities compared to others. Central Park was almost like real country with lakes, forests, cliffs, and all enormous. Gramercy Park was small but clean and pretty, and only people with keys to the gate could play behind its metal bars, like high-class birds in an aviary. But our park was neither wilderness nor sanctuary. There were more trees than now— horse chestnuts, and many plane trees dotted with seedballs and grimed sparrows—but still not enough to make a forest or even woods. There was nothing much to explore. When we climbed between the iron fence rungs looking for jungles and anxious for treasure, we found only dull shrubbery and parched grass full of chewing-gum papers. The angry park man was our only tiger, and burnt black carbon sticks from the arc lamps were as near as we could come to treasure: they made pretty good chalk. But we were not discouraged that all our sapphires turned out to be pieces of magnesia bottle and all our silver crumbs of tin foil. We continued to search. And children are more fortunate, or perhaps less cordial to disappointment than adults: where no treasure exists for their discovery they will invent it, or add the concept of value to something hitherto unclaimed. It is their necessity not so much to find what they are seeking, as to find the thing to seek.

The sour park earth was earth after all; real worms lived in it, real roots confined it, and real stones were dredged up by time to its sooty surface. Our eyes were caught at last by a glitter that had possibilities: small pieces of rock, full of mica flakes. Ira took one in his hand; it was soft and he crumbled it. On his palm the particles were separate and shimmering, a powder of gold. The importance of the fact struck us at the same moment.

"This stuff is valuable," Ira said tensely. "Listen, we can grind this stuff up and make gold dust out of it. Find some more, go on, hurry up, and then we'll take it somewhere secret and experiment. I'll find some, too, and listen! Don't let anyone know! Don't let them see and don't explain."

Close-lipped, secretive, I searched the dingy grass for mica stones and found a pocketful. Ira did too. We met and made our way to the side of one of the shrubbery triangles somewhat out of the main stream of activity; there was no true seclusion in that park.

Stamping on the stones was unsuccessful. Ira found two larger, harder rocks and we squatted on our haunches—obedient to the last, we did not sit—and pounded stubbornly like Navajo squaws preparing meal. The soft stones crumbled and crushed, becoming a glittering powder; some silver, some gold. Our industry and noise attracted attention, everybody came and asked us what we were doing.

"Go away," we said. "We are busy."

Nobody thought of going. More came. Even the girl we hated because her hair was clipped close like a boy's. Ira said she had leprosy and to keep out of her breathing range. Her upper lip was always chapped and we further despised her because not only did she not know she was an outcast but she believed herself to be a leader.

"What are you doing?" she asked, and when we didn't answer she kept it up. "Hm? What are you doing? Hm? I said what are you—"

"We're making an explosive. We're the only ones that know how to handle it," Ira said. "It's so deadly that even its name is deadly. We don't dare to say it, we have to call it Shush."

"Oh, you do not," she said, but edged away a little on her skates, and we kept on pounding.

"Shush is a good name," I said.

"I know it," said Ira.

Our friends now wished to take part in our enterprise but we were not ready to let them. On that first day it had not yet occurred to them that stones exactly like these could be collected by anyone. We still had priority, and the piles of glistening powder grew. We were clumsy then, we hurt ourselves and wasted material, but we soon became skillful.

For we were diligent. Each afternoon we set out like laborers, armed with hammers, potato mashers, pillboxes, mason jars, or other receptacles. We spent hours squatting and pounding, gathering up crumbs between chapped fingers. We became expert and selective: the Shush was assayed and graded, that with too much dirt in it being thrown away or offered to the innocent. We traded in pinches, and used it for barter; we hoarded and gloated, for as the Shush became currency we became misers. Each evening we returned, soiled, weary, with bruised thumbs and dirty fingernails, but in the jars and pillboxes there was a little more of the precious dust for which we had toiled and haggled. The linings of our pockets gave way beneath the weight of rocks, bright particles shone from the seams of our clothes.

"My God," cried my mother, sweeping the rug with the hearth broom. "It's getting so you leave a shiny trail like a snail wherever you go!" She was becoming frantic with stones and all the bottles and boxes marked: "Valuable! Do not throw out!!" She threw them out anyway from desperation while I was in school, so I became crafty and hid them in the pockets of shoe bags and under the lion-paw bathtub where nobody ever looked.

"But what can you do with the stuff once you've got it?" sighed my mother.

"Trade it for other things; chalk and things. Gum," I said; for who could explain the simple luxury of gloating? Lying on the bed at rest time holding the medicine bottles up to the light, letting the sunshine sparkle on the different types of Shush, the gold kind, the silver kind, the blackish kind? On rainy days, or when I had a cold, I stayed indoors and painted pictures of beautiful Mary Pickfords with wings and crowns of stars. The crowns and wings were lightly, inaccurately coated with glue, sprinkled over with Shush, and set by the radiator to dry. The effect was dazzling: a gallery of Made in Germany prewar angels. I sent them all to Ira.

But the greatest joy was in the toil of acquisition. In school each morning I looked forward to the long spring afternoons when I and my fellow treasure-hunters would return to our labors. For by now the madness was on the whole park. Nurses cynically extracted work implements from the foot of perambulators on arrival, and gave them to older brothers and sisters, and on departure they put them back again without complaint. "It keeps them quiet," they told each other. "Anyway it keeps them busy." People from the ages of two to twelve were to be seen daily in the grass lots, bent over searching, and later down on their knees, bent over pounding. The little shoeshine boys put aside their wooden boxes and pounded, too. The supply of Shush stones was nearly exhausted in our park and replacements had to be brought from Central Park on Saturday excursions. Someone imported stones of superior grade from a place in Morningside Heights which were procured by individuals at a high rate of exchange in jacks, marbles, and dolls' eyeballs. The pounding continued and accelerated. Everywhere a smashed glitter on the pavement gave evidence of the prevailing industry and avarice which, as June approached, reached fanatic and fantastic proportions. Ever since that time I have felt that I had some understanding of those derelict prospectors who are only happy shaking the pan by the summer stream, staking the claim on the rocky hill; who, oblivious of age, arthritis, respect of relatives, peace of mind, and good blue suits, are cajoled and driven by the phantom sparkle that dances between the bloodshot retina and the hard-bosomed world.

How did it end? The summer came. We all went away to our separate fields and beaches and forgot about each other for months, and when we came back—it was the same every year —we were all different people, with more teeth, or fewer, and bigger feet, and other ideas. We never spoke of Shush again, and Ira and I were no longer brother and sister but rather cool acquaintances.

The major part of life has passed since then; yet to this day when I see mica-crusted rocks glistening in the sunshine my first feeling is a lust for possession. For an instant I would like to be down on my haunches in Washington Square, chewing my tasty hat elastic and pounding for riches with Ira.

A Little Talk

From the ages of eight to eleven I went to a school on West Eleventh Street which was conducted by two maiden ladies: Miss Carstairs and Miss Monahan. A Dame's School, my mother was fond of calling it. It was situated in an apartment, where the ladies also lived, in a brownstone building which even then must have been getting on in years. The architect who built it had had a curious taste in ornamentation, for on the balustrade by the front steps there lay a creature, carved in bold relief, which had the head of a lion, the body of a serpent, and the wings of a bat; and just above the entrance a bearded head of stone gazed down, leering like Priapus. We never considered any of this odd or ominous, and once inside the school all was reassuringly academic: a realm of blackboards and maps. There were plants in the windows, and a locked glass cabinet containing summer trophies brought by returning pupils: sea shells, tattered luna moths, and birds' nests.

The apartment was of an old-fashioned sort, having as its spine a long narrow corridor upon which all the rooms opened. The first three of these at the front, or south part of the building, were the classrooms; and the rest toward the rear, each with a closed door, comprised the mysterious region where the ladies had their home.

Miss Carstairs was the principal and founder of the school. She was a small energetic woman with a clipped pedagogic way of speaking, gray hair, and a pair of vigorous black eyebrows above alert black eyes. Authority was her characteristic; authority and a loyalty to justice which we all sensed and respected. We liked her, but we feared her a little, too; and it seemed right and fitting that arithmetic was the subject she taught.

Her partner, Miss Monahan, was another type: a soft cloudy woman with fine taupe hair rolled onto her head in a sort of cushion, a pince-nez, and moles that were the same color as her skin. I cannot remember that she ever smiled or frowned. In my memory her permanent expression is one of gentle preoccupation. Miss Monahan taught art and basket-weaving. Every Tuesday when we came to school the apartment was pervaded with the smell of the wet reed that lay soaking in the bathtub and handbasin of the one bathroom. Weekly throughout the winter, year after year, we wove our baskets: square ones and round ones, pot-shaped and vase-shaped. All of them were taken home, praised, used; found their way, eventually, to the dust and obscurity of closet top shelves, and thence to limbo.

On Friday we were given instruction in drawing and painting. Seated at our desks, our Milton Bradley paintboxes at the ready, we attempted to copy exactly the subject set before us:

a halved apple on a plate with a knife, two daffodils in a glass of water, a sprig of catkins. High lights were stressed.

There were three other faculty members on the school staff: Miss Waldbridge, who taught history and geography, Miss Mariner, the English teacher, and Mademoiselle, who, of course, taught French.

Miss Waldbridge was a plump, fair woman with two deep dimples that looked as if they had been forced into her cheeks with a knitting needle. She did not swallow often enough, and as she lectured her voice would become more and more foggy and cumbered, and her pupils would keep swallowing for her till their throats were dry. She had a bold carefree way with the pronunciation of foreign names. To us the capital of Brazil was a city called Rio Dudgeon-iro. Then there was Ben Airs in India, and Bonus Airs in Argentina; and I was a married woman before I knew that Ponce de Leon was not called Ponts de Leeon. Still on the whole I liked Miss Waldbridge's classes and I loved making those maps on which one glues a piece of cotton to the State of Georgia to show what it is there for, a corn kernel to the State of Kansas, a bit of coal to Pennsylvania, a bit of orange peel to Florida. (In those days geography was full of such summary dismissals.)

But our favorite class was English, because Miss Mariner, who taught it, was our favorite teacher. She was young and beautiful, with a sort of graceful asperity; her eyeglasses glittered like crystal, and her shirtwaists were always crisp and scented. Her handwriting, which we tried unsuccessfully to copy, was exquisite, original, a little affected, and her hand, if one should touch it, was cool as a rose. But though we all worshiped her, it was not only for her approval that we worked hard at our "compositions"; she was a good teacher, devoted to her subject, and able to kindle in us a true desire for expression.

Mademoiselle was the only teacher any of us disliked, and

I feared her, as well. She came into the school the autumn I was nine years old. Before that there had always been Monsieur, who looked like a drawing by Boutet de Monvel with his eloquent eyes, his mouth perfectly round as he sounded the "eu" in words like "*peu*," and his mustache, tender as a moth, spread out on his upper lip. His teaching style was serious and polite.

Mademoiselle was a very different matter. She was a wiry, thin little woman with glasses, and a crimson skin pulled tight over the bones of her face. The threads of her dark hair were crimped and gathered into a tiny knot at the nape of her neck. She always wore a black dress with a black crocheted shawl across her shoulders for she had a Gallic caution concerning *courants d'airs*, and when she entered the classroom any window that might have been open was closed at once. Her lessons must have occurred late in the morning for I remember the noon sunshine strong against the windows where the narcissus bulbs were sprouting in their pebble beds. I remember the laconic clang of the radiator, and the way the air in the room was slowly permeated and at last overwhelmed by the aroma of the garlic which Mademoiselle must have eaten at every meal. Now and then she would take a metal box from her pocket, extract a tiny pastille, and an odor of peppermint would then be added.

The choler of Mademoiselle was something I have never seen before or since. As she sat in the classroom you could sometimes feel the struggling of her temper as if it were a living separate entity: the Spartan's fox, perhaps, or an adder in the bosom. She limped badly and it is possible that she was often in pain; and I can imagine, now, that her life was a thing of penury and fear. But being children we did not take these possibilities into account, or even consider them. Her rage when it broke over seemed to us arbitrary, terrifying. She would cry out, gesture, tremble, and her narrow face would darken to the color of claret. Her little gold earrings would shake desperately (and never at any time did they seem an expression of vanity or gayness).

I was the one she hated most, though I never knew exactly why. I was a quiet child, reasonably well behaved, though poor at concentrating, at least as far as studies were concerned. My parents, being artists, did not like to have me dressed in a conventional way; I was a victim of smocked pongee and quaint collars, and my hair was trained to lie on my shoulders in long limp curls like the fingers of empty gloves. I was pale and given to daydreams. "Always dreaming!" sighed my teachers with patience or exasperation, according to their moods. "Wake up, Elizabeth, wake up, for pity's sake!" Probably it was just this quality, vague and lackadaisical, which was intolerable to Mademoiselle's sharp practical temperament.

One April day, when I was ten, I goaded her, unwittingly, to her greatest outburst. The air was mild that morning and full of spring: everyone was yawning, or struggling with yawns. The lesson droned along and along and I looked at the well-known boring illustrations in my French grammar: the photograph of the Champs Elysées, the photograph of the Place de la Concorde, both apparently taken many years before on a dull Sunday afternoon. Even the picture of Joan of Arc was boring; moreover she looked plain. With my pencil I began to draw her some ringlets around the edges of her helmet; and I improved on her mouth. I was so absorbed in my work that I did not hear Mademoiselle ask me a question, and she must have asked it more than once, for suddenly she slammed her book on the desk with a thunderclap. "*Mon Dieu!*" she cried hoarsely, almost exultant in her rage. "*Mon Dieu, que tu es* BÊTE! You stupid, stupid girl! Draw, draw, dream, dream! *Imbécile! Idiot!* Your parents pay their money that you should learn and you do not learn, you do not listen, you do not *try!* What I must do to make you pay attention? Shout? *Shout? SHOUT?*"

Miss Carstairs hearing the noise hurried into the classroom to find her French teacher in full cry, the chords standing out on her neck, her eyes dilated; she seemed to be lurching dangerously on the brink of something; a scream or a fit.

"Mademoiselle! *Mademoiselle!*" cried Miss Carstairs. "Control yourself! *Control yourself!*"

Muttering, shaking her head, panting, Mademoiselle gradually subsided. Miss Carstairs stood watching her, leaning forward, her hands braced on a desk top. Her black brows looked stern. But in a moment she turned to us and smiled reassuringly. "Today we'll dismiss the class a few minutes early," she said. "I think we're all a little tired this morning." It was the only remark I ever heard her make that might have been called appeasing.

A week or two later our class was given an examination in English. Since this was my best subject I felt reasonably confident that I would pass, in spite of the cumbrous rules of grammar that would have to be rolled from the path.

When the day came the questions on the blackboard seemed easier than usual, and I worked my way through them without much trouble. In fact I finished before anyone else. Pleasantly exhilarated by this I sat back in my chair biting toothmarks into my soft cedar pencil and surveying the labors of my classmates. There were sounds of hard breathing, sighs, the sibilant rustle of many pencils, the scruff, scruff, scruff of rubber erasers. Near the blackboard, facing us, Miss Mariner stood in a beautiful attitude, like a symbol of fate, her head bent looking at the watch in one hand, and the other held poised above a little round bell. Time was running out. Mademoiselle, chewing something, came and stood in the doorway, waiting to take the next class.

Beside me, at the desk to my right, sat Margaret Smith, a girl I liked. My tranquil eye fell on her paper, read it, and detected there what seemed to be a glaring error.

"Listen, Marg," I whispered hastily, leaning near her, "you've got the answer to number six all wrong. It's supposed to be—"

But at that instant Miss Mariner's fateful hand struck the bell. The peremptory note rang out, despite the groans of laggards.

"Time's up, girls. Fold your papers."

"Oh, fish," said Margaret. "Now I'll have to let it go."

Mademoiselle brushed by me as she entered.

The next morning, just before French class, Miss Carstairs came to me and asked me to go back with her to "the living room, for a little talk." This room one never saw except in cases of nosebleed, or sudden indispositions, or when it was necessary for Miss Carstairs to speak privately to one of her pupils. Nothing was the matter with me that I knew of, and I followed her down the long narrow hall wondering what I had done; if my parents had suddenly been killed, or what.

The room was a comfortable darkish place adorned with Morris prints, bayberry candles, and hammered brass trays, probably from Ben Airs.

Miss Carstairs drew two chairs cozily together and we sat down.

"Elizabeth," she said gravely, "we are very fond of you here in school . . ."

This terrible beginning prepared me for the worst, though I had no idea what that was to be.

"It's just because we *are* so fond of you that I feel I must have this little talk with you now." She looked at me very intently. "Do you know what I am going to speak about?"

I shook my head, mutely.

"Elizabeth, I was told . . . it was brought to my attention . . . that yesterday during your English test you did something unworthy of you."

I stared.

"You were seen, dear; it happened. You were seen looking at another girl's paper." Miss Carstairs cleared her throat, and shook her head at me gently. "Elizabeth, in a test, if we don't know the answers, we don't . . . we must never . . ." She paused, probably casting about in her mind for some better word than "cheat." "We must never *borrow* our answers from someone else. That is not honest."

I sat silent. I swallowed on a dry throat, and said not one word in my own defense. After all I had looked at Margaret's paper, and probably in such a circumstance it was just as wrong to give advice as to steal it.

Miss Carstairs went on a little longer, with phrases like growing up "fine and clean and straight," and thinking of my "fine, wonderful parents," and so on. But at last she leaned forward, took my hand in hers, and said: "I know I'll never have to speak to you like this again." Then she stood up and I was released, just in time for French.

The classroom seemed very light and bare after the dimness of the living room. My classmates turned and looked at me with friendly, malicious curiosity; but they would never learn a word from me. They were solicitous and passed me notes; and Mademoiselle was remarkably gentle in her manner.

The next day when the examination papers were returned to us they showed that Margaret's answer to question number six had been correct. So had everybody else's. I was the only one in the class who had given the wrong answer.

The Eclipse

That January morning in 1925 was clear and cold. At seven thirty the rising bell rang with its usual hellish brusqueness, and I huddled deeper in my bed trying to pretend sleep back again—trying to pretend, as I did every morning, that I need not get up until I wished. My three roommates were groaning lumps under the covers. The room was freezing; our breath was steam on the air, and the water in the glass beside my bed had turned to ice.

It was Nydia's turn to close the windows, but it was only after repeated insults and commands from the rest of us that she finally had the fortitude to hurl back the covers and make a majestic sprint, like a young Demeter in pajamas, to the casement windows.

"God!" she said, banging them shut. "Sweet God Almighty!" and she lunged back into bed.

Marcia reared up on her elbow and reached for her glasses. "God," she agreed. Then she yawned on a note of resignation and put her feet out, searching for her fur slippers, which peered like a pair of hamsters from under the bed. "Well, kids, it has to be done," she said. Marcia had the twin advantages over the rest of us of being the most sensible and the most sophisticated. Many boys had kissed her and she had been invited to the Dartmouth Carnival.

Nydia, with her sapphire eyes, was the most beautiful; and Terry, who at this hour of the morning was still only a hump and a pigtail in her bed, was the richest, and was further set apart from the rest of us by the fact that she was seriously in love and was loved in return. She was always receiving letters with such messages on the envelope flaps as "Wait and Hope," or "Darkest before Dawn," for her love was star-crossed; her parents thought her far too young for serious romance, and perhaps her wealth was an obstacle, too.

As for me, I was the least sophisticated and the least sensible, the least beautiful and the least rich; also I was not in love. However, I thought fairly well of myself nonetheless; the huge aurora borealis of adolescent hope assured me that some day I would obtain these five major requirements with very little trouble. They would just happen to me nicely when the time came.

Marcia slip-slapped back from the bathroom, looking well-scrubbed and smelling of toothpaste.

"O.K., kids, up!" she said tersely. The two characteristics mentioned, added to the fact that she was older than the rest of us, endowed her with a quality of leadership, almost of generalship, and sometimes she could be ruthless. Now, for instance, she stooped and stripped the covers away from Nydia. "Get up," she repeated, "today's the great day."

Seeing that peace was at an end I leaped out of bed, and from Terry came signs of slow upheaval. Terry had brought four fur coats to school, and two of them—the beaver, and the leopard with the red fox collar—were draped on her bed as coverlets. More than any of us she hated to get up in the morning, and often we contrived to sneak her breakfast to her, but today this was out of the question.

"Who wants to see the damned old eclipse, anyway," she grumbled. But she grumbled amiably; she was never really cross. She reached for the leopard coat and put it on over her nightgown, then thrust her plump feet into the high-heeled patent-leather pumps she preferred to bedroom slippers.

Nydia dressed silently. She was always silent and remote before breakfast. I shivered and complained volubly, and Marcia, butting her head into one of her many sweaters, replied with comments deploring but philosophical.

The breakfast bell rang too soon. It always did. After that we were allowed five minutes leeway, and every day it was chaos and scuffle. This morning even Terry was goaded to haste.

"Where are my shoes, where are my damn shoes—oh, here . . . what did I put them on the bureau for?" she moaned distractedly.

Only Marcia was ready in plenty of time, neat in her skirt and sweater, her argyle-patterned wool stockings and saddle shoes. Nydia daringly applied some Roger & Gallet pink pomade to her lips, then rubbed it off again. She gave herself one last cold passionate look in the mirror and made a hook-shaped gesture with the palm of each hand against the blond sickle of hair that pressed against each cheek. At her side, sharing the mirror, I struggled with my own hair, which I had pinned up for the first time a few months before. After weeks of practice I had succeeded in arranging it so that it looked more like cloth than hair. It was wrapped around my head in broad turban bands. No hat would fit over it, and my scalp was stung with hairpins all day long, but I thought it looked handsome and unusual, though I cannot remember that anyone ever concurred in this opinion.

"Girls! Girls!" cried the housemother looking in at the door. "This is absolutely your last chance! Hurry!"

I cursed my turban of hair, which, this morning, had turned out lopsided and rakish, but there was no time to change it. I plunged after my roommates, who were already jostling and thundering down the stairs to the dining room, where, for once, we could all enjoy a leisurely breakfast without thought of classes. Since there was to be a half-holiday in the universe, it was suitable that we should have one, too.

After breakfast was the time to straighten the rooms. We all made our own beds, and mine, when finished, looked rather lumpish owing to the fact that the copy of *Wuthering Heights* that I had been reading the night before, by flashlight under the covers, was still in the bed. It is possible that the flashlight was there, too, though I have forgotten.

Each week one of us was delegated to do all the sweeping and dusting of the room, and this week it was my turn. My roommates departed heartlessly and I was left alone.

The room was large, with a bow of leaded casement windows and a window seat. The house and grounds had once been the estate of an heiress, and there was a certain grandeur about the size of everything, and the bathrooms were extremely luxurious for a boarding school. Most of the luxury and grandeur ended there, however. In our room there were two immense bureaus, and four narrow metal beds on which no two bedspreads were the same color or pattern. On the bureaus, among hair brushes and bottles of the kind of perfume people give teen-agers, the rather flattered photographs of parents and younger brothers looked out self-consciously. On the window seat there was a portable Victrola (we called it a "Vic"), a stack of records, many magazines, and a few stuffed animals. In the cabinet beneath the window seat there was, as I knew well, a jug of cider, which instead of turning hard was turning disappointingly to vinegar; there were several boxes of soda crackers, and a jar of Hyppolite marshmallow whip with a spoon in it. There may have been a bitten dill pickle in waxed paper—there often was—and there was almost certainly a pound box of salted peanuts. Tucked far back out of sight, beside the copy of *Flaming Youth,* and Balzac's *Contes Drolatiques,* there was a package of cigarettes, and some matches.

I cranked up the Victrola and put on a record of the "Hymn to the Sun," from *Coq d'Or.* It was the most wonderful music in the world. When that was finished I put on a record of Ukulele Ike singing "I Can't Get the One I Want," and it was just as wonderful. Listening happily I went about the business of straightening the bureau tops, blowing the dust off vigorously, and arranging toilet articles in a sort of pious symmetry. When I brought out the broom and carpet sweeper I realized for the hundredth time how fortunate we were. To the furnishing of our room Terry's mother had contributed a huge pink Oriental rug with a fine delicate pattern and the bloom of silk. It must have been very valuable; old Mrs. Purchase, a lady of culture who had endowed the school with a library and then come along to see that it was taken care of, was always creeping in to study the rug and shake her head, and once we had even found her down on her knees with a bottle of Carbona, cleaning off a spot. Aside from its beauty and its silky warmth to our bare soles, we appreciated it for another reason. As I moved about on it now, making casual swipes with the carpet sweeper, the whole rosy expanse crunched and crepitated gently under my feet, for in its passive way the rug had saved us many minutes of time, and much dull traffic with dustpans.

In the middle of the morning the bell rang again, sounding strange at this unaccustomed hour, but we all knew what it meant, and began getting out our sweaters and galoshes.

"Who wants to see the damned old eclipse, anyway," said Terry again, pulling on the leopard coat. "We'll just stand around freezing for *hours* and *hours*."

"Well, I prefer it to *Julius Caesar*," I said. "I certainly prefer it to *physics!*" The truth was that I felt the wildest excitement at the prospect of seeing a total eclipse, but knew it would be naïve to say so.

Nydia and I each borrowed a fur coat from Terry; Marcia had her own coonskin one, made just like a college boy's, without any shape at all. Terry borrowed a hat from Nydia and I loaned one to Marcia, and she loaned me an extra sweater and Nydia borrowed my angora mittens. We all wore our galoshes unbuckled because that was the way to wear them, and when we walked down the stairs we jingled like a detachment of cavalry.

Outdoors a procession of station wagons had been commandeered from the parents of day pupils. An air of revelry prevailed, causing the younger children to leap in the air and squeal.

Finally, after the usual delay and confusion, we were packed into our appointed places in the station wagons, and the journey began. The world was white with fallen snow, and we could look deep, deep into the bare-boned woods that edged the road. I remember the jovial metallic snack-snack-snack of the tire chains, and the starling chittering of the younger children in the car behind.

Miles away we stopped at the foot of a great bald hill where the view was said to be the best in the region.

"You mean we're going to *climb* the thing?" said Terry. She detested exercise, and her techniques for evading basketball practice were formidable.

"I bet I'll be winded," Nydia murmured with pride. She had been known to smoke as many as twelve cigarettes in one day.

We toiled up the broad flank of the hill through deep snow. Our unbuckled galoshes clapped and clattered and caught at the hems of our skirts; snow slopped over the tops of them. Erratic as squirrels, the younger children darted and zig-zagged, while the teachers and parents, their overshoes sensibly fastened, forged steadily ahead with the Spartan philosophical gait peculiar to adults on an outing with children.

Luckily the day was fair, though already a strangeness had come into the light, like the light in dreams, and it was bitterly cold. The dome of the hill, when we reached it, was immense—a vast rounded plain. Against the waste of white the scattered groups of people seemed diminished and at the same time sharpened in outline; adjuncts to nature, like the figures in Breughel snow-pieces.

Mr. Blunden, the science teacher, had built a fire up there. He and Mr. Ripley, the math teacher, were squatted beside it, smoking pieces of glass. My feelings about Mr. Blunden were mixed. Every December for the last three years I had taken the part of Mary in the school nativity play, and Mr. Blunden was always Joseph. Three times he had led me across the wilderness of the assembly room, in front of the thrilling, rustling audience, to the door of the secretary's office, where we were denied shelter for the night, and from there up the broad staircase to Bethlehem on the landing. Here we disappeared for a moment and then, curtains parting, I was seen beside the manger wearing a gilded buckram halo and gazing earnestly into a 150-watt Mazda bulb. The world would be green for an hour afterward, and I remember feelings of exaltation and gratified ego; but somehow I could not help wishing that somebody else, not Mr. Blunden, might have been Joseph.

He and Mr. Ripley handed out the pieces of blackened

glass and strips of exposed negative. We had been warned not to look at the sun without one of these protections, and now, holding up my sooty glass, I took my first look.

The sun was in crescent, an imitation of the moon, a humble step down from power. It looked no different from the several partial eclipses I had seen in my life, and I was disappointed.

The younger children played in the snow and screamed. Nydia giggled with Tom Frank, one of our classmates, and Marcia, in low tones, was giving advice to Hank McCurdy, another classmate. She loved to give advice, especially to boys. Terry paced to and fro, lost in her own thoughts.

The light was weakening and weakening and the cold growing: a deathly cold. We began to stamp and beat our hands together, and when a thermos of hot cocoa was produced there were cheers.

"Why couldn't it be coffee!" murmured Marcia in disgust.

Whenever I looked at the sun through the black glass it had grown narrower; and finally it was little more than a sickle of reddish light. Then less. Less . . . Still less.

And now the miracle took place. I dropped my glass. Across the snow, suddenly, ran streamers of shadow and iridescent light, wavering bands turning and turning in an unimaginable wheel of rays. What was happening? There was a startling impression of swiftness, as if something—someone?—hastened forward. The sky darkened abruptly. A great still coldness dropped onto the world, and all around its edge there was a band of orange light, like the instant before sunrise on all the horizons of the earth at once.

"Look up! Look, look, look," whispered Terry.

In the deep sky where there had been a sun, we saw a ring of white silver; a smoking ring, and all the smokes were silver, too; gauzy, fuming, curling, unbelievable. And who had ever seen the sky this color! Not in earliest morning or at twilight, never before had we seen or dreamed this strange immortal blue in which a few large stars now sparkled as though for the first time in creation.

At some point I glanced for an instant at those nearest me. I had never seen before, nor have I since, the expression of total awe on the faces of a crowd; all turned upward, arrested, self-forgotten, like the faces of revelation in old religious paintings.

There were tears on Terry's cheeks, I remember, and Carla Cudlipp, a fat pragmatical girl, was on her knees in the snow in an attitude of prayer. Even Miss Lagrange, a battle-ax if ever one lived, was trembling all over like a frightened child.

But I watched them for no longer than a second; it was more important to watch, to try to memorize, that marvelous smoking circle of light, where all too soon the blinding edge of crescent appeared and one could look no longer, and had no wish to look.

We were quiet going down the hill again; even the younger children were quiet. "Gosh," said Marcia, and sighed. It seemed as suitable a comment as any.

All of us were frozen with cold, subdued, spotted with soot. The world once more was muted in the queer dreamlight. Nothing seemed familiar.

"But suppose you'd never seen the sun set in your life," said Nydia suddenly. "Suppose you'd never seen a rainbow. It would be the same thing; you'd be just as—as dumfounded. You know, you'd get this same terrific kick out of it. I mean it's not a phenomenon or God or anything, it's just that the moon gets in front of the sun once in a while; just a natural thing. It's only that you hardly ever get to *see* it."

"Yes, but gosh, when you do see it, it makes everything else seem more wonderful," I said. "It's as though they let you in on the secret for a minute or two; I mean it's sort of as though they let you remember how it all works and how *wonderful* it is!"

But it was beyond my powers to express what I meant. I fell silent, trying to recapture in memory the exact impression, the exact sensation, of that instant when the universe had seemed to open like a door before me, or my own eyes to open and behold for the first time.

We felt that we had been away for months. Everything in our room, when we returned, looked childish, trivial, and cheap.

Marcia hurled her coat on the bed, smoothed her sweater down on her hips, sighed.

"I know! Let's have a snack before lunch," she said, brightening. Then she went to the cabinet and brought out the box of crackers and the marshmallow whip, settling comfortably on her bed with them, spreading the crackers with a lavish hand. She held one out to me. I had not realized I was so hungry, and went on eating when the others had stopped, although I knew it would be a matter of minutes until the lunch bell rang.

Nydia went to the mirror and refreshed herself at her own reflection for a while, then she turned to the Victrola, cranked it up, and put on a record called "Brown Eyes Why Are You Blue?" Recklessly, she reached in the cabinet and brought out a cigarette, lighted it, and began dancing slowly with her eyes closed, as if asleep. She had learned, by diligent application, to hold the smoke in her mouth for a long time and then let it out gradually through her nostrils, and she did this now. She looked very worldly. I sat watching her as I crunched steadily through the box of soda crackers.

Terry, oblivious of all, was writing yet another somber letter to her Jack (she had written three the day before), and Marcia was polishing her nails with a buffer; the pearl ring she had been given on her sixteenth birthday gleamed and winked rhythmically.

There was a noise in the hall outside our room, and Nydia's

blue eyes flew open. She stubbed out the cigarette on the sole of her shoe, tossed it into the wastebasket, and stood a moment listening, holding her breath and fanning away the smoke. Then she laughed.

"Come on, Lib," she said to me, holding out her hands. "Let's dance. You need the practice; you're still terrible. I'll lead."

Humbly and doggedly I did my best to follow. Terry looked up and smiled at us vaguely from her remote place. Marcia watched my feet. "Try not to trudge," she said.

Little by little we were curing ourselves of wonder.

The Sandals of Monsieur de Flandre

In 1928 when I was an art student and my mother an illustrator, we lived for a year in Paris in a small apartment near the Invalides. It was on the second floor of an old U-shaped building five stories high, which embraced a broad flagged court containing many tubs of laurel and cats. On rainy days this court resounded with the mallet-clatter of the concierge's sabots and the harsh sweeping of her broom, as she took advantage of the weather to clean the stones. A powerful odor of Eau de Javelle would join the smell of rain.

Our apartment contained three narrow rooms, a kitchen, and a gigantic clothes closet. The front windows looked out on the court, and the rear ones onto a garden which belonged to two Russian ladies living on the ground floor. This garden was one of our reasons for taking the apartment; it was large and sunny, furnished with tall old trees, graveled paths, iron armchairs, and a sibilant stand of bamboo. Roses grew on the stone walls, and next door there was a convent of cloistered nuns whom we often heard singing in their chapel, but of whom we never saw a trace. It might have been an establishment of ghosts for all we could tell.

The furniture in our apartment was good, though heterogeneous, for the landlady from whom we had sublet it was an antique dealer and used the place as a sort of storage warehouse for excess merchandise. We had Empire chairs, a Victorian sofa, a Provençal chest, and a dining table with an ornamental enamel top which celebrated the works of Meyerbeer. The walls were covered with plain pink paper and hung with dead clocks, curios, water colors and silhouettes. In the morning the sunshine came flooding in from the east, across the garden, and in the afternoon from the west, across the court, and the pink walls would take light. As winter came on there was always a fire in the grate, and the charcoal *boulets* glowed red-hot, like a nest of phoenix eggs.

My bedroom, adjoining, had some unusual features. Besides the polished parquet floor, black marble fireplace, and elegantly mirrored cabinets, it contained, except for the w.c., every plumbing fixture in the place. The bathtub and bidet were concealed behind a screen of printed linen, but there was no way to hide the handbasin awkwardly situated by the window, or the copper water heater which stared like Medusa from a point halfway up the wall.

This mechanism, called a *chauffe-bain*, was as sinister as it appeared. Whenever my mother or I applied a match to it, it would blink, tremble, hiss, and suddenly shoot forth yard-high flames of a celestial blue. Only the busy concierge could control it, and for this reason most of our baths that year were taken in cold water. The tub was unusual, too. It had been hand-painted, inside and out, with a material resembling stucco.

Despite these eccentricities I loved my room. Its window opened on the garden, and at night before I slept I could hear, above the distant bleating traffic, the rather melancholy rustle of bamboo, and that sound of night wind in branches which always, even in cities, seems a country utterance. To these would be added, from time to time, a lonesome gulp from one or another of the plumbing fixtures that shared my night.

The building was more than a hundred years old. It was well made, and the walls were thick; still, one could hear one's neighbors sometimes, especially early in the day before other noises had taken up the air.

At seven in the morning, for instance, there was a great clamor of clocks; everybody in the building seemed to have a clock that rang, and now they would all begin announcing the hour, none ringing in unison, one overtaking the other, all different in their pacing and chiming; and then, sometimes just after the bustle of the clocks, sometimes just before, but rarely at the same moment, would come the grave, fatherly pronouncement of the bell of St. François Xavier.

On the top floor where the poorest people lived the taxi driver's children now began their coughing. They had whooping cough that year, one child taking it from the next, and that one from the next. Perhaps it was for this reason that they, like the cloistered nuns, were never seen by anyone. *Plein air* was not for them.

Above the court, on the third floor, the young bank teller was already standing by the open window, polishing his wife's shoes and whistling Puccini. They lived a good part of their lives beside this window: earlier he had shaved there, staring steadfastly into a bracketed mirror and wielding a two-legged razor that might have belonged to his grandfather; and at noon when he came home to *déjeuner* his wife would be leaning out watching for him and swinging the lettuce basket. And often after that the window was closed and the blind drawn down.

On those mornings, if it was not raining, I might also hear the crunching of gravel and the exotic sound of Russian words, for the Russian ladies, like gardeners everywhere, could not wait to be out in the morning to see what magic might have changed their garden overnight.

These ladies, the Mesdemoiselles Kuprin, had fled during the revolution and had since worked hard for their living: one at needlework, one in a *maison de couture*. Yet though they were pinched for funds, aging, and hard-pressed, their household had that casual, expansive atmosphere that pervades the scenes in stories by Turgenev and Chekhov. Someone was always paying them a visit, and often they had parties, well attended by taxi drivers who had been generals and florists who were princes of the blood. Somebody would have brought an accordion or guitar, and on those nights there was a sound of constantly interrupted music, and a henhouse gabble. The Kuprin parrot squawked until its cage was covered, and I, leaning on the grille in my dark window, watched the guests strolling the paths, smelled their tobacco, listened to their deep voices, and entertained vague, inaccurate thoughts about Old Russia and the Nevsky Prospekt.

Besides the parrot the Kuprins had a dog named Sasha, a cat named Yasha, or something that sounded like that, and a servantwoman named Masha. During the day somebody down there was always opening a door and calling one of these names, accompanied by the parrot. One never knew which would respond: sometimes it would be the cat streaking out of the bamboo; sometimes the fat dog waddling forward with his eyes nearly closed and his tongue at half-mast; sometimes the old servant groaning up from her weeding. And often even these three were in doubt and all converged on the house together.

Of the other tenants I remember only two. One was an

ancient *avocat* who had a small office at the foot of our stair. He kept the door open and one could see him, day in, day out, seated at his desk in gravy-colored gloom, hat on his head, hands folded, and never a client in sight. Perhaps the fusty air of his office was sweeter than the air of home, and occasionally another old man would come to have a game of chess with him. There they would sit, booming their throats clear like Mexican pigeons, and, now and then, speaking.

The other tenant, to whom I shall come in a moment, was a different matter altogether.

Our landlady, Madame Redon, was, as I have said, an *antiquaire*, and it did not seem out of the way to her to remove from our apartment such pieces of furniture as she might want, without consulting us. On the wall, for instance, among many other things, there was a great framed shadowbox containing a clockwork scene of the coronation of Czar Alexander II. The setting was the interior of a cathedral, perhaps St. Isaac's in St. Petersburg, and in the foregound was a throng of cardboard figures dressed in noble attire. At the turn of a key all the ladies in crinolines and ermine, all the gentlemen in orders and muttonchop whiskers, would quaver slowly round a track in an agued ritual, and from his throne the little czar would bow and bow. We were very fond of this curiosity and enjoyed showing it to our friends, but one day when we came home we found it gone, and nothing to replace it but a rectangle of darker pink on the rose-pink wallpaper.

Again, returning from a country weekend we found that our Empire chairs had turned to Biedermeier, and once when we were having a dinner party we were interrupted in the middle of it by the arrival of two giants in aprons and kobold's caps. They brought in an invigorating smell of crates and told us that they had come to remove the dinner table.

"*C'est Madame Redon qui a commandé*," they explained. My mother, whose French was a masterpiece of improvisation, was able by this means, strengthened with outrage and a large tip, to get the kobolds off the premises without the table, and the next morning she called our landlady and made matters clear. Nothing was removed again.

One thing that Madame Redon had left behind and might have done better to remove was a former protégé, a young actor from the Comédie-Française named Monsieur de Flandre. One would imagine a young actor from the Comédie-Française to be something very different from what this young man was. I remember him well. He was tall, slender, sloped forward like a melting candle. His black hair was smooth and looked wet, and his face seemed strangely closed or guarded, emphasized in this, probably, by the thick lenses of his glasses. His little eyes slipped to and fro behind them, cold, blue, and diminished. He was a silent creature, only nodding when we met him on the stairs, and we were always meeting him on the stairs. We never heard him before we saw him because he was in the habit of wearing pink rubber sandals. He lived on the floor above us, and of course we had no idea that he still had a key to our apartment.

One day, starting through the door, I nearly knocked him over on the landing.

"*Pardon, Mademoiselle,*" he said, slipping smoothly into our foyer and smiling. His teeth were the same color as his face. He managed to make me understand that he had at that very instant been preparing to ring our bell. He had come, he said, to offer a suggestion for my consideration.

I nodded apprehensively. Though I understood French fairly well, I was barred from speaking it by the grim verb forms I had had to struggle with in school. They stood before me like so many rigid iron gates, and by the time I had decided which was the proper one to use, the occasion for using it was gone forever.

Monsieur de Flandre's proposition concerned this problem

directly. He said he had come to offer to teach me French. At the same time, he pointed out, he could pick up a little English, and in this way we could share many happy hours of mutual benefit.

Still standing in the foyer, gripping my pocketbook, nodding and smiling insincerely and committing myself to nothing, I managed simply by the strength of wish to get him out the door. I would as soon have taken lessons from a conger eel.

"I suppose the poor chap needs the money," was my mother's comment, given reluctantly; even her charitable nature was unable to warm to Monsieur de Flandre. "I wonder what they pay them at the Comédie-Française?"

I said nothing. Such was my adolescent vanity that I thought I knew another reason for his offer.

However, it was not made again and I soon forgot about it. My life was busy and absorbing.

I was studying at that time with many other American girls at an art school in the Place des Vosges. Every morning, leaving my mother already at her drawing board, I would go to the taxi rank on the Boulevard des Invalides and climb into one of the old red cabs that smelled as if it had come from a stable instead of a garage. The hurrying streets that we divided were all dazzled and slanted with the dusty topaz light peculiar to that city on fair mornings. Rattling and bleating, the taxi would curse its way along the quais, past the Île de la Cité where Notre Dame squatted jeweled among its buttresses, across the Île St. Louis with its lifted trees, and on and on through the cluttered, yapping, gilded streets. I remember a great feeling of well-being on those mornings. All thoughts of myself and my future were dusted with an illusion of gold, just as the city was.

The Place des Vosges, when we reached it, was still half in shadow, still quiet. It was as if I had taken a taxi into the seventeenth century, and in a sense I had. But when I entered the stately building that housed the school, the twentieth century was restored to me. On the second floor I could hear the nasal chirping of my compatriots. They were healthy girls who maintained a realistic objectivity toward their work; they kept at it (and some were talented), but they seldom talked about it. Their conversation was all of "darling boys," and of late hours at Joe Zelli's, Chez Mr. Finney, Les Ambassadeurs . . .

When school was over, as the winter deepened, we used to go in batches to the Palais de Glace and skate to the sound of scraped old waltzes. One glass of *grog Américain* was sufficient to keep us swooping like eagles until suppertime.

In January some friends of my mother's came to Paris, and she was out of the house nearly as much as I was. It was very cold. The sky closed down over the city, a stolid, pork-fat gray, and lights were turned on at three in the afternoon. One day late in the month, I woke up with a cold and decided not to go to school. My mother had an engagement and left the house about eleven. I took my book to her room and settled on the chaise longue by the window because the telephone was there and gave me some mild feeling of companionship.

There had been a light fall of snow in the night, and down in the garden old Masha was clearing the paths with a baba jaga's broom of faggots. Her head was done up in a shawl, and her feet moved slowly in big wads of overshoes; she steamed like an engine. Sasha, the dog, poked along at her heels, snuffing the snow half-heartedly.

I felt cozy and uncomfortable, the way one does when nursing a cold. In the next room the grate-fire hissed and stumbled; it made me sleepy to hear it. And then there was another sound, a quiet sound that did not belong there. I turned my head quickly. Into the room on his pink rubber sandals walked Monsieur de Flandre.

My heart took a great fall in my chest and then started

leaping. I stood up and backed away. I could feel my eyes dilate, and even as I reached for the wall behind me, even as the scream grew in my throat, a corner of my mind took cold note of the fact that I was reacting exactly as I had often seen Blanche Sweet or Leatrice Joy react to the carnal advance of Wallace Beery, or some other villain.

But I did not need to scream after all. For in that instant that holds so still in memory I saw that Monsieur de Flandre was quite as horrified as I was.

"*Ah, Mademoiselle! Pardon! Pardon, je vous en prie!*" And in a high, ringing voice he explained that he had thought we were out, that we were both out; that he had heard a noise in our apartment and felt that he should investigate, that it was in our best interest to investigate . . . "*et puis, Madame Redon m'a donné la clef. Voici! La clef, vous savez, Mademoiselle? Pour la porte, vous savez?*" He held up a key, waved it at me, as if this in itself explained everything, and all the time he, too, was backing away, backing away as he chattered, across the living room, into the foyer, through the door, and the door slammed. And then, even in those silent sandals, I could hear him running up the stairs to the third floor.

The first thing my mother did, when I told her, was to rush to her jewel box; and I belatedly rushed to mine, though it contained no item worth more than a dollar ninety-eight. Nothing was missing. Next she went to the clothes closet to see if her fur coat was still there. It was; (black and white ponyskin). Then she called the concierge to have the lock changed.

"I simply can't understand it," she said. "With that key he's probably been here more than once, but what in the world can he have *wanted?*"

We found that out at the first of the month when the telephone bill arrived. It amounted to two thousand francs, which in those days came to about eighty dollars. Listed on the bill were more than twenty calls to Bordighera in Italy.

"Good God! What's this?" cried my mother.

"Monsieur de Flandre," said I.

"Why! But the *scoundrel!*"

After a moment, as the shock died down, she said: "Think how he must have lain in wait up there! Every day, practically, he must have been skulking on the landing, waiting for us to leave. Ugh! But of course I won't have to pay it."

Yet in the end she did. Monsieur de Flandre in his mackerel-smooth fashion had prudently slipped into limbo on the thirty-first of January, leaving a month's rent due, and no address. Madame Redon refused all responsibility for him, cordially agreeing that he was a villain, and disclaiming any knowledge of a duplicate key. As for the concierge, Madame Pellerin, she was very sympathetic, but when she saw the bill, with the many Bordighera calls, she looked at us for a moment, quivering, then threw back her head and showed all her beautiful ferocious teeth in a big French laugh. Monsieur de Flandre, it seemed, was courting an Italian lady, a widow and former tenant, who had, in fact, been the cause of the final break between himself and Madame Redon.

"*Elle n'etait pas belle, cette dame Italienne. Pas belle. Pas jeune. Ah, mais Madame, qu'elle etait riche, riche, riche!*" sang the concierge, her hands clasped together in happy awe.

"Yet I'm the one who must foot the bill for the courtship," said my mother angrily. But in a moment she laughed, too.

I don't think I laughed. I'm sure I did not. The recollection of my crouching, backward, Leatrice Joy retreat across the room was like a blister on my memory. It was years before I told anyone the story.

A Green Shade

In the summer of 1929, thousands of Americans surged into Europe on a crest of riches. If they had not the air of conquerors, they had at least the confidence and the objective eye of those with money to spend. My mother and I, on no such crest, shoaled with the lesser minnows, and washed up on a hillside in the English Lake Country.

The British friends with whom we stayed had recently rented a Georgian villa—a graceful, somber building with tall French windows, urns on the terrace walls, and fireplaces that smoked wet smoke. The view from all the windows was so ponderously green that we felt submerged and oppressed—particularly as we always saw it through a mantle of rain. Except for one day, it rained without stopping for three weeks, day and night, though with varying degrees of intensity. When the waterfall downpour lessened to a mild drizzle, we all, hosts and guests, rushed for our mackintoshes and gum boots and sloshed out into the drowned green Wordsworth country. The trees there had solid domes of rain-nourished leaves; wet lambs jumped and tumbled in the emerald pastures; and the roses on the gray stone walls hung heavy as fists. In the soaked lanes of the village, geese swayed and honked in little armadas, and puddle water rose up from the wheels of every passing cart.

On the one rainless day, the cold blue sky was stocked with gray-bellied clouds that took their time warming themselves at the sun. "What a *lovely* day!" cried our hosts, shivering on the terrace. "Too *lovely*, really, isn't it?"

It was beautiful, perhaps; the hills came into view clear-cut for the first time, and a little lake that until then had been agate gray or olive drab now stared out blue and stony as a Prussian eye. To me, the scene seemed hostile, unfamiliar, and I was glad to have the rain return.

In the house, I read poetry or picked out music on a Bechstein piano that was beginning to cough with damp. Sometimes I sat in the orangery as rain boomed on the glass roof, and wrestled with the deadly crossword puzzles of Torquemada, in the *Observer*. I did well if I filled in three words during a morning.

I was nineteen years old, and everyone else in the house was forty-five or more. All of them, being old, retired early, of course, but I kept my light on very late, and read in bed. There were no screens on the windows, and often, in out of the pouring night, a random crane fly would come lurching. Crane flies look and sound like huge, nightmare mosquitoes, and though they have no sting, they also lack a proper sense of direction. Aiming for the bedside lamp, they would miscalculate drunkenly and slap against my cheek or ear. I learned to slay them in midair with flung copies of the *Saturday*

Evening Post, the *Tatler*, and other large, glossy periodicals, which I kept handy for the purpose. My hostess, on coming into my room one morning, was surprised to see the floor tessellated with magazines. "What do you do with them, dear —use them for steppingstones?" she asked me.

"I throw them at those bugs," I explained. "You know— those ghastly bugs that zoom in at night."

"Elizabeth!" My hostess was shocked out of her characteristic gentleness. "Don't say *bugs!* In England, 'bugs' is *not a nice word!*"

What could it mean, I wondered, but I did not ask. I had discovered that the number of things I did not know was of such magnitude that silence, combined with an alert expression, was the best refuge. Before this visit, I had never heard of a salmon trout, or a mountain called Helvellyn, or even of Dove Cottage. I had not known the meanings of such words as "Palladian," "motet," and "dialectic," or of such names as Joynson-Hicks, Chambertin, Kafka, and Baby Austin. In the evenings, when we played parlor games, I was the one who could be counted on not to know the source of "The multitudinous seas incarnadine," or the author of *The Critique of Pure Reason*. Everybody else seemed to know, although I had doubts about my mother.

Besides ourselves, there were other guests from time to time. I remember a kindly retired major who played Beethoven sonatas in a way that made them sound very masculine and British, and took a twenty-mile walk each day. Another guest was a man so learned that when he spoke, which was often, I felt muted and deformed with ignorance. He relieved me of the Torquemada puzzle each morning he was there, completing it with very little trouble before luncheon. Among other things, he was an authority on wine. Our host had ordered a case of little-known wines from Boulestin's, and each evening at dinner, a bottle having been opened and poured, the rest of us would wait while the learned guest took the first sip. Then, in suspense, we watched as he swallowed it delicately, staring off at some remote point, communing with flavor, judging. "Not quite valid, but likable," he said of one, I remember, and another time he shook his head reluctantly. "I don't seem able to make anything *of* it." I marveled at these pronouncements. As far as alcohol was concerned, my palate had been trained on a Prohibition mixture of gin, orange juice, and white of egg.

One morning, our hostess came into the drawing room with a look of pleasure and excitement. "Darlings, what do you think!" she cried. "We've all been invited to Catbeams! For lunch! On Tuesday week! Lady Clara just rang up."

Catbeams, it turned out, was one of the Great Places—a castle, really, that belonged to a local earl. When we heard this, my mother and I were also pleased. We had seen castles in France and England, but always among strangers and in the cold commercial wake of a paid guide.

When the day came, I dressed in a manner I considered appropriate. I put on the treasure of my wardrobe, a dress handed down to me by a fashionable friend. It was a Chanel wool jersey with a pleated skirt and a matching cardigan. I chose brown-and-white sports shoes and decided to wear no hat, and felt well pleased with my appearance. My hostess came rustling into the room, wearing a navy-blue taffeta dress, a fox fur, and a hat with a water lily on it. I saw from her look that something was wrong. "Isn't this all right?" I asked. "Shall I change?"

"Well, dear, I think something a little—perhaps a little *dressier*. You know you have so many *pretty* frocks," she said.

After she had left, I put on the dress I had worn up from London. It was brown silk, with a skirt that ended swiftly at the kneecap and a broad belt that girdled the buttocks. A

large bow was perched at my wishbone. I wore a double
choker of baroque pearls and a brown hat that had been
modeled on the wrapped headcloths of the Pharaohs; it gripped
my brow severely and swept downward at each side in a
hound ear. Beneath the hound ears of my hat, my own ears
were buttoned to my head with large pearl earrings. The final
touches were a pair of wide-meshed dark-brown stockings of
a sort called fish-net, and *glacé* kid oxfords with three-inch
spike heels. Just to be certain that everything was perfect, I
sprayed myself liberally with Coty's Emeraude perfume.

My hostess, returning, was delighted. "That's just the thing,
dear," she said kindly. "It does pay to take a little trouble,
doesn't it? After all, you know, these people are *County*."

I did not know what "County" meant, though I assumed
it had something to do with the peerage, but I refrained from
asking, as I had refrained from asking about "bugs."

"I say!" our host called from the foot of the stairs. "It's
gone one, for God's sake!" And soon, wearing a look of exasperated endurance, he herded us, rustling and teetering, into
his car, and we were off on our subaqueous drive up hill and
down dale.

The waterproof at the sides of the car leaked, and my
mother and I huddled together in the middle of the back seat,
viewing, between the stern, motionless head of our host and
the agitated hat of our hostess, the unfolding of yet more and
more green country, like an endless and gigantic tossed green
salad.

Catbeams, when we reached it, was all a castle should be,
though minus turrets—long, low-lying, with a crenelated roof
line and mullioned windows. The yew trees were ancient and
well groomed; the lawns looked as if they had been woven in
Lyon.

The butler who opened the door was sickle-shaped with age.
He ushered our host in one direction, while Lady Clara, who

came to greet us, ushered the rest of us in another. She had a lovely, aging face disfigured by a powdering of pure white exactly on her nose and exactly on her chin. She was cordial and warmhearted, and held my hand as she introduced us to a gathering of women in a large living room. I heard not a single name; my mind was registering the fact that all the women who were not wearing tweed suits were wearing versions of the Chanel cardigan dress. Those who were not wearing brogues were wearing brown-and-white shoes. Nobody was wearing a hat. My mother, my hostess, and I crackled like turkeys as we settled on a couch.

I looked about the room. The furniture was heterogeneous, but all of it was good. The chintzes did not match, but they were old and pleasing. There was a vast, shabby Aubusson carpet on the floor, with various small rugs afloat on its bosom, perhaps to cover up worn spots. Suddenly, I heard a clatter of claws in the bare hall outside, and a pack of ten or fifteen dogs —like the furniture, heterogeneous but all good breeds— burst into the room at a gallop, silently circled it twice, and departed as they had come, leaving the rugs up in mole tracks. Nobody commented on this or seemed to notice it at all.

I sat mute, a smile fixed to my face, watching and trying to sort out the women—some young, some old. There were two very young girls, and there was a beauty whom I imagined to be about my own age. *She* was wearing a Chanel dress, and her hair and complexion had the ineffable glow that comes from perfect health and a childhood spent in wet weather. Her only make-up was lipstick and a dab of azure on each eyelid, above each azure eye. I watched her, fascinated and jealous, and soon, sensing my attention, she came and sat beside me on the arm of the couch. "How are you enduring our ghastly climate?" she inquired pleasantly.

"Oh, I really love it," I lied.

"Yes, well, I mean to say it's all right for us, of course, we're born with a set of gills, but for anyone used to sunshine—"

"But I'm having a marvelous time," I insisted. "The scenery is so marvelous."

"If you like green, I suppose it is," said the beauty. "For myself, I prefer purple. Scotland is the country for me. Purple everywhere. This time of year. But the weather is just as bloody there as it is here. Funny how one doesn't seem to mind."

She talked easily, without self-consciousness; she was an expert at dealing with the awkward pause. In the course of her conversation, I learned that she was married, thirty years old (Thirty! Until then, that age had seemed to me as remote and undesirable as the age of fifty), and the mother of three children. I saw that my incredulity was pleasing to her; her laughter was kind and gratified.

At last, Lady Clara rose and led us to the dining room, where a huge table had been set. Behind every second chair stood a footman in eighteenth-century livery. Just as we were taking our places, into the room, one by one, came eight or ten of the most distinguished-looking men that I had ever seen. I felt my jaw go slack. Among them I recognized the benevolent, weary face of Lord Cecil, which I had often seen in photographs. The men were not very young, any of them, but each looked exactly like himself and no one else, and their tweed clothes seemed organically a part of them, as only the tweeds of Englishmen ever do. With them came the local vicar, a stout, unsmiling little man who cast one chilled glance in my direction and then never looked at me again, though he was seated at my right throughout the meal. He probably did not like Americans, or my hat may have frightened him.

Nobody was actually introduced to anybody else, though as the men ambled in Lady Clara muttered their names—before most of them there was the word "Lord"—all in a row, rapidly, as if they were rather shameful. The vicar turned as much of his back upon me as he could, and addressed himself winningly to his hostess. He spoke of Rupert Brooke. How he managed to arrive at this subject so rapidly I have no idea. At my left, there was a tall, oldish-young man with diluted blue eyes and a melancholy blond mustache. He, it turned out, was the husband of the beauty, and after our first glance of mutual alarm he began to make kindly, dogged efforts to draw me out.

I do not remember much of our conversation, but I remember other things—that the cuffs of the footmen's coats were frayed and darned, that there were three kinds of wine, and that the table was adorned with great, healthy pyramids of fruit in silver cornucopias. At the far end of the table, a little boy and his governess made their appearance. Lady Clara's family followed the pattern of many whose photographs I had seen in the *Tatler* and the *Sketch:* the noble mother, weary-eyed, the several daughters in a row at her side, ranging from adolescence down to pigtails, and at the very last (God has been good!) a little boy. In Lady Clara's case, I learned, five daughters had come first.

Across the table, the beauty sipped her wine and chatted easily with those nearest her, while my partner and I worked dutifully to keep our conversation alive. Question and answer, question and answer—the material of polite interrogation at length was nearly threadbare. And then, toward the end of the meal, he came up with one more question. "And politics," he said suddenly and hopefully. "At home, I expect you take great interest in politics?"

I was shocked. "Good heavens, no!" I cried, aghast.

In the little silence that followed, I saw the beauty across the table smile at her husband—a tiny, irresistible flicker of mirth. Of sympathy? Of derision? At any rate, it was intimate without coquetry—companionable, above all.

The cornucopias of fruit were removed from the center of the table and handed round, and I heard the vicar quoting, "The nectarine and curious peach into my hands themselves do reach." His voice was sonorous and self-respecting, and after he had said the words he looked at his hostess expectantly, but Lady Clara's amiable smile was vague.

"Andrew Marvell. 'Thoughts in a Garden,' " I said promptly, not without pride. After all, I had steeped for weeks in the *Oxford Book of English Verse;* it was right that it should bring me some returns.

The vicar affected not to hear; he did not even glance in my direction. But his ear betrayed him, anyway, by turning crimson. It was not I who was supposed to recognize the source of his felicitous quotation, which perhaps he had been planning all through the meal.

I was now completely put to rout, and sat in silence, horridly aware of my Pharaoh hat and my three-inch heels. I could feel the nasty meshes of my stockings creeping on my calves, and every time I drew a breath I was reminded that I had used too much of Coty's Emeraude. I thought of the beauty and her husband, of that conjugal smile of intimacy and shared response, and I found that even if the smile had been at my expense, I wished most earnestly someday to smile like that at someone else; and for the first time it occurred to me that I had been rather slow about growing up.

Now, half a lifetime later, I sometimes think of that day and those people, and idly wonder what became of them. The lords will be dead or doddering, their ladies old, if alive. What happened to the little boy, who would have been old enough to fight in the last war? What fortune met the beauty and her husband? As for the vicar, I have a feeling that he must still be quoting poetry to the nobility somewhere in that green, teeming land. I have noticed that snobs are apt to live longer than the average, and, on the whole, enjoy good health.

The Caterpillar Summer

In a sense, the caterpillars that invaded our lives were introduced to us by the fish. Years ago, my two elder children and I spent a summer in Wisconsin, living in a house that looked out onto a great valley bisected by a river—a broad, smooth road of water that smoked with mist on chilly mornings and lay calm as spilled milk on warm, still days. It carried a flotilla of tufted islands and, though slowly silting up, was comfortably fed by many little tributaries—springs and streams—all well furnished with fish. Fat, comatose catfish dozed in brown sloughs, and in the streams and the many ponds that stippled the floor of the valley were crowds of bluegills and chub, pumpkinseeds, crappies, sheepshead, and bullhead. I learned their names from the ten-year-old in our family, who learned them from the farmers. And we learned their flavors, too. Every day, the ten-year-old went fishing, and, since he was a lucky fisherman and this was a war year, when meat was scarce, nearly every day we ate his catch.

The following winter his little brother, in nursery school, refused the Friday fish at lunch.

"You don't like fish?" his teacher asked; and he replied austerely, "Only chub."

Each summer morning I watched his older brother set off with his rod and his creel, in which a canful of night crawlers and a package of Spam sandwiches jounced together companionably, and each evening I would watch him returning, stopping on one leg to scratch his bites, half a dozen fields away, then coming on again until I could see his serious face under his farmer's hat, and his bare stomach with its aboriginal dirt stripes where he had slapped at midges. The fishing rod would glance on his shoulder, and from one hand a good-sized fish tassel would almost always hang glittering.

Now and then, besides the catch, he would have brought something else: a bunch of pennyroyal, because I liked the smell of it; a fat, ear-shaped tree fungus; or a fresh-water clamshell from the river, pearled and rosy.

One day, he picked a sprig of wild grape from his creel and held it up. "Lookit, Mum," he said.

Clinging to the stem, under a chewed leaf, was a stout, bold-looking caterpillar, like a tiny diesel locomotive. It seemed made of cinnamon-brown velvet, and on each of its sides was stenciled a row of light baroque medallions. A great, wrinkled cowl surrounded its little noncommittal insect face, giving its head a false look of size and splendor.

"What in the world?" I asked.

"I dunno," the boy said. "Some kind of worm, I guess. I think it eats this stuff, this grape that it's on. I'm going to keep it and raise it."

"Just so long as you keep it *in* something," I said.

The creature ate many times its weight in greenstuff, prospered, and grew fat. Now, each day, the boy brought home a new caterpillar or a whole set of caterpillar siblings: green, yellow, and brown ones, furred or bald, striped or dotted, large or small. Once, he brought a single huge green one—a Cecropia, we learned later—garishly studded all over with beads of red and blue and yellow.

Each species went into its own glass jar capped with mosquito netting and furnished with an abundant supply of whatever the caterpillar had been eating when abducted. The boy's room, as you could hear if you stood perfectly still in it, rustled continuously and crackled and crepitated with the tiny sounds of the caterpillars' industrious voracity. Eating was their entire existence at this stage; they ate to the point where they literally burst their skins and stepped out of them, a leg at a time, like somebody getting out of a six-legged union suit—and then, as a rule, they ate the skins. Often, they emerged as new personalities with completely different colors and adornments. Their life was one of constant metamorphosis.

Meanwhile, the creatures were always running out of food, and usually running out of it at night, when the collector was blandly asleep in his bed. I was the one who went cursing down through the dark orchard, following the lurching beam of my flashlight and stumbling over apples in the wet grass, to the vegetable garden, where I could find a cabbage leaf for the cabbage worms (or larvae, as I was now urged to call them) or parsley for the swallowtails. The monarch caterpillars ate milkweed only, and often my mind would have to range furiously over remembered terrain searching for the milkweed that was nearest but never near enough.

And soon I, too, was caught up in the boy's new enthusiasm;

the creatures were interesting and sometimes beautiful, and there was something fascinating about that fanatic appetite and about the ritual progress from egg to larva to chrysalis to winged insect. We began our study from the beginning, my son and I, learning empirically, for the only butterfly book we could get hold of had been written for young children and was both incomplete and sentimental.

When the first captive, the cinnamon-brown diesel, stopped feeding, and began striding and rippling around its prison with a gait not unlike a strip-teaser's, we guessed that it wanted to make a cocoon, and gave it a suitable twig, which it ignored. "Heavens, do they have to have special kinds of *twigs* now?" I complained.

We tried several others. The diesel refused them all, and, if one can say it about a caterpillar, began to take on a haggard, raddled look of strain. I had an inspiration. "Maybe it burrows!" I said. "Do they ever burrow?"

"I'll go get some dirt," said my son.

We put earth into the jar, and the diesel flung itself upon it with an air of none-too-soon and disappeared from sight in a matter of seconds.

One of the monarchs stopped gnawing on milkweed and began to stride. Unlike the diesel, it accepted a twig at once, and had soon incased itself in a lovely cradle—a pale-green pendant freckled with gold and hung on a dark silk thread. As this chrysalis ripened, it darkened until it was nearly black, and two or three weeks later the monarch came forth, black and orange and crumpled like a squashed tiger-lily petal, and then slowly, slowly, in a sort of trance, breathed itself to perfection. We felt somehow responsible for this, proud in a new way, and we released the butterfly to the August day feeling as benevolent and successful as a pair of deities.

Sometimes the cocoon makers rejected their quarters

and, unobserved, contrived to push up a corner of mosquito netting and ripple away to preferred sites, chosen who knows how or why? Caterpillars were at large in the house; it was no place for the squeamish. I found a cocoon in my city hat, left for the summer on a closet shelf. Jade monarch pendants appeared on ceiling and bookcase, and a certain door could not be closed for weeks because of two cocoons lined up beside the hinge. No one was allowed to disturb any of them—not even Mrs. Jameson, who came twice a week to clean. (She was a massive, realistic woman who always worked barefoot because shoes "crowded" her, and who exerted a malignant power over the radio; whenever she touched it, it would begin guffawing hillbilly music.) Her response to the cocoons was disciplined but unmistakable. A glassy, reserved look came into her eye, and she said, "Sometimes I dunno . . ." and gave a cold laugh.

But the collection grew. The great Cecropia caterpillar knitted itself into a mitten of silk as big as a fist, and so did our one Polyphemus. The earth burrowers, we found, had turned into black sarcophagi; we dug one up and shook it, and, on the palm of my hand, it bowed spectrally in its cold case.

By now, my eye, like the boy's, searched twigs and branches whenever I was outdoors—searched the ground for the green pellets euphemistically called "traces," or lighted with pleasure on a clutch of butterfly eggs, like the tiniest seed pearls stitched onto a raspberry leaf.

Eventually, we sent for a good book on lepidoptera and learned the names of everything we saw, pronouncing all of them wrong, but happy in our study. In my memory, that whole summer is a queer synthesis of fish, caterpillars, butterflies, and great snatched views of valley and river and clouds, all overlaid with a sweet, hot smell of cake (for that was the summer, also, that I learned to bake) and set to the tune of scratchy English folk dances. These were the only records in the house, and the children never wearied of them. I used to comb my hair, make beds, and cook meals compulsively keeping time to the jaunty antique rhythms that filled the house. It was a lovely summer; we were all sorry when it ended.

Our return to New York was complicated by eccentric additions to our luggage—cartons with jars half full of earth in them, and frail, ungainly packages of cocoon-bearing twigs, for though the monarch and the swallowtail had emerged from the chrysalis in short order, others would lie sleeping and changing throughout the winter. Naturally, we were not going to leave them behind.

When we got home, it was as though news of our activities had reached the city ahead of us. On a twig of the ailanthus tree in the dooryard of our house on Twelfth Street was a large rural-looking Cecropia cocoon, and the lace vine that hung like Rapunzel's hair down the front of the house was strung with odd gray lockets. "Cynthia cocoons!" cried my son in a transport, dropping everything on the pavement and climbing onto the iron railing of the stoop. I held on to his trouser band as he wavered and lurched, plucking down the ones within reach.

That winter, among his assortment of maps, comics, model war matériel, empty pop bottles, chemical phials, birds' nests, and sea shells, there were jars and a bristling of twigs. And soon these were half forgotten, never looked at, accepted as part of the barnacle incrustation that lined his room, while the summer that had produced them receded and diminished to that golden, unlikely medley in the mind that one never quite believes in as the winter grows.

One Saturday night in February, my husband and I came home late from a gay party. We creaked and giggled our way upstairs. My husband went into the bathroom and turned on the light. Instantly, he leaped out backward with a ghastly sort of throttled yelp. "Look at that! What the hell is *that?*"

With my scalp prickling and my jaw dropped, I peered over his shoulder. Circling the dangling light, something huge and velvety was flapping and veering.

"Oh, heavens! It's the Cecropia moth!" I said. "It's hatched much too soon. The warm house, I guess."

"Damn thing flew right into my face," said my husband. "Felt like a pair of suède gloves. Right in my face!" He seemed upset. "Why can't that kid take an interest in something else?" he wanted to know. "Something like football or mechanics, that can't startle ten years off you in the middle of the night? Butterflies!" he said. "Moths! My God! Get him out of bed and tell him to cope with it himself."

"I can't," I said. "He's away for the weekend—remember?"

"Then we'll have to put it out the window."

"Oh, we couldn't!" I said. "It's sleeting. I suppose we'll have to kill the poor thing. It will just bang itself to pieces in the house."

"I'm not going to brush my teeth with it slapping around in there," said my husband. "The hell with brushing my teeth." He went into the bedroom.

I stood watching the Cecropia. It is one of the most beautiful moths, dark, with fringed antennae, and wings that are trimmed with crescents and crimson bands. It cannot eat. It has been dedicated by nature only to the perpetuation of its kind. By some mysterious means of communication, it must find a mate; that is all it must do, all it is for, and the time allotted it is very short. I did not want to kill it. I went to the bedroom door. "You do it," I said to my husband. His reply was a short laugh, in no way mirthful or encouraging. He got into bed and closed his eyes. "Well, I'll do it tomorrow," I said, and went back and shut the bathroom door.

After a while, it seemed to me that through the walls of

two rooms I could hear the moth thumping and blundering to get out. It was impossible that I could actually hear it, but it sounded to me as loud as footsteps, or the beating of Poe's telltale heart. Finally I put some cotton and carbon tetrachloride in the bottom of a jar and went into the bathroom. The Cecropia was in the tub, flat on the porcelain; already it was frayed and damaged. I picked it up and closed it in the lethal chamber. After one short spasm, it lay still on the cotton. I thought with horror of all the other cocoons in the boy's room which would probably also hatch too soon.

They did. One never knew what to expect when one went into the place. There might be a scratching and rustling among the toy tanks and tractors, and one would find a crawling, heavy moth, its wings still birth-shriveled, or there would be a pair of new Cynthias, taupe and pistachio green, clapping out an aerial duet. As spring came on, and when the boy was not there to stop me, I used to open the window and shoo them out.

By the next summer the moths and butterflies had outranked the fish in my son's favors and remained in first place for many years. By the time he was in college, he had gone so far into new regions that I hardly knew what he was talking about. (And now that he is a grown-up geneticist I do not know at all.) He spoke lovingly of things like ecology and taxonomy, and as he chewed a Hershey bar, a pizza pie, or a meat-loaf sandwich, since he was a dedicated eater, too, his fascinated eye translated genetic charts that looked to me like the pictographs of a lost civilization. His closest companions shared his interests (one of them, he told me, was doing very interesting work on fat digestion in the cockroach), and they talked for hours on the telephone about paratypes and clinal gradations. Already theirs was the passion, and the elegant language, of science. As for me, I continued to linger in the hinterland of ignorance, where a butterfly's life span still exemplifies the legend, with all its symbolism, of the lowly creature, ugly, obscure, and tethered to an appetite, which in the end attains transfiguration and an airborne freedom.

Dragons, Policemen,
and Early-Morning Screams

Things have changed since this piece was written. New York University has gobbled up the house we lived in; the baby mentioned will soon be graduated from school; and Dominic no longer walks the park as if he owned it, and never will again. One thinks of other changes, too. There is no doubt that now the scream is heard more often in the hostile night, the horses' hoofs more rarely, if at all. The fire engines long ago regained their voices, but with a difference. Yet there are certain things that stay the same and will forever: morning is one of them, early morning, when children wake up in their cribs; and hope, irrational and persistent, wakes up with them.

On the north side of Washington Square, west of Fifth Avenue, the old red Rhinelander buildings have been broken down and thrown away. Where they stood there is now a raw yellow gulf. Machinery gnashes in it all day long, and at night the wind roves through it and lifts the ancient cellar dust. But east of the Avenue the familiar row of Georgian brick houses stands as sound and solid as it has for the last hundred years, its pillared porticoes and marble-paved vestibules still intact. When I was a little girl playing in the Square, these houses were nearly all owned by private families, and though that was many years after the invention of the motorcar, it is my impression that horse-drawn vehicles—elegant victorias and barouches—were the only ones that ever waited before these mansions. One glimpsed starched maids, wearing caps, when the front doors were opened, and children's whitened shoes dried on the upstairs window sills.

It never occurred to me then that someday there would be apartments in these houses and that I would live in one of them myself, and set out a child's white shoes to dry on my own sill. But for more than a year I have lived there, and every time I come home and close the big front door behind me I am glad. Gone are the barouches and the maids in caps, gone are the sturdy fortunes and the peace of mind, but the houses testify that such things once existed. The houses neither shake, rattle, nor peel. The rooms are large and lofty, the doors are solid mahogany, the plumbing is splendid if uncomfortable, and the floors are beautifully inlaid. Best of all, these houses face the south; the sun pours into them all day, along with a constant babble from the park.

Washington Square has always played a part in the winters, springs, and autumns of my life. My childhood afternoons were spent in it, and I am the sort of old-timer who can remember when every circular patch of bare ground was a tree and Garibaldi had no fence around him. My children, too, have played here, and it was here that they took their earliest steps, mastered the pedals of their tricycles, first slapped—or were slapped by—their contemporaries, and learned the basic laws of ownership. Here they rooted and squabbled in the dank sand piles, and wore out the seats of their snowsuits on the slides while I stamped my chilblained feet and shivered. On the first warm day of the year, when they shed their heavy jackets, I watched them and remembered exactly how it felt to be so light all at once, so released, so drunk with freedom and the arrival of spring—for somehow spring does manage to make its way through all the dirt, chewing gum, bread for pigeons, and pigeon droppings, and accomplish its green, if dingy, transformation.

Most daytime aspects of the park have been known to me for a long time, but now, since I live so close to it, I have discovered new ones. My bedroom windows overlook it, and when I wake up in the morning I see the sky and treetops, and pigeons lumbering through the early air. The sun, at that hour, has not yet risen high enough to clear the buildings. When I go to the window and look down, the Square is shadowed and nearly empty. Only the first dog-walkers are abroad, and the first daily maids on their way to work. Yesterday's newspapers turn idly on the ground, like flounder on the bottom of a bay. The park attendant has not begun to spear them. He will spear them, though, down to the last clumsy, captious piece; I never yet have seen him stoop to pick one up.

After a while, the university students will come hurrying with their briefcases. They are so young that they're apt to run even if they aren't late. The office workers hurry, too, though they wear their haste with a difference. If you were blindfolded, you could tell how close to nine o'clock it was, just by the number and tempo of their footsteps. Dominic, however, does not hurry. He comes into the park at a philosopher's pace, with his shoeshine box clapping against his back and his overcoat flapping. His cap is pulled so far forward that he has to hold his head back to see out from under it at all, and his eyes are as blue and bleached as an old mariner's.

Here and there are little clots of pigeons. They are public poultry, and someone is always feeding them. The benches gradually become lined with men who are old or idle, reading newspapers. The park attendant trundles past them with a barrow full of twigs. From ten o'clock till dusk, when the playgrounds are locked up, the Square is just as I have always known it.

Night, though, is a different matter. I have never had a chance before to study the aspects of a park late at night, and for this new opportunity I am indebted to my youngest child, who is teething. From time to time, he wakes in the small hours, makes his complaint, accepts ministration, and lapses into sleep again, while I am left behind, cracklingly awake. Often I am drawn to the window, to look out at the large, neatly spangled Square. It is usually deserted; a policeman clears it each night at a little before midnight, and it is a pleasure to watch him as he stands there, bawling banishment at the loiterers. He is powerful, tremendous. He glitters. His buttons, his badge, his nightstick, all shoot forth rays of light. He is mighty, like a red-hot furnace, his voice is joyful, and the people are blown out of the park by it as if by a blasting wind. It is a little while before they seep back in.

But when I go to the window hours later, they have drifted off again of their own volition. Cars veer silently along the extension of Fifth Avenue that cuts the Square in two. The last dog-walkers are gone, the last loud teen-agers, and the kissing couples in the shadows, and all is as still as it can be in the center of a city. It was not always so quiet here, even at this late hour, for there are nests of fire engines in the neighborhood, and until last summer, when they were robbed of their sirens, one or another group of them was always howling through the streets. Hearing them constantly like that, and not often seeing them, I found it difficult to remember that they were vehicles driven by men bent on rescue. The hysterical noises they made seemed to have nothing to do with men. I imagined a crowd of adolescent she-dragons foregathering, their brazen ringlets flying and their nostrils dilating. With the high, impulsive screams and giggles of female puberty, these metallic hoydens clanged through the night to some far trysting ground, and returned as raucously.

Late at night, when the Square is silent, it is possible to hear, between the sounds of river whistle and taxi horn, the wind sifting through the branches—a memory of country sounds—and the stars are just as clean and brilliant and remote as country stars.

Opposite my window, on the south side of the Square, a single lighted word shines. Day and night, it is always there, red as rubies or live coals. The intervening branches make it illegible from my window, but because it is constant, solitary, commanding, one feels it could be anything—the key to revelation, the single word that will resolve the puzzle. Actually, I have walked across the park to read the word, and it is "Garage." Still, it is reassuring in its way, if only because it is always there.

Standing at the window very late at night, I sometimes think of all the pretty fables about nighttime parks. I remember Peter Pan, and the elves and quaint philosophers and ghostly girls who are supposed to make these parks their kingdoms after dark. (The rats are never mentioned.) But in Washington Square, instead of Peter Pan, we have the drunks. After they have spent all their money and are as drunk as they are going to be able to get, the park provides space and costs nothing. Also, it seems to revive some memory of their childhood. When they come into it, they often want to play children's games—tag, leapfrog, hide-and-seek. Their condition adds a hazard to their play; they fall a lot and stumble, and no course is broad enough for their races. If they do not bump the trees, they bump each other, and, leaping over the low iron hoops that edge the grassplots, they sometimes fail to leap high enough and are slammed to earth. They are eerie as they run and leap, silent and concentrated, middle-aged, shabby leprechauns.

Now and then the policeman comes into the Square again. "O.K., bums! Scram! Get out!" he bellows, and off they go, blown along the gutters, frayed and ruined as last year's leaves.

Silence is restored. The big, pearly lights seem to have no stems, to be balanced gently among the branches. Nothing moves except the creeping newspapers. The traffic lights wink green and then wink red, though sometimes there's no traffic to obey them. If morning is close, there is likely to be a long time when there is no sound of a footfall or a voice, and it is still dead-dark. In the country, every rooster would be stretching up his neck and crowing, but here, for a little while, sound is suspended, and all the laws that guard the day seem lifted or forgotten. It is a no man's hour.

One winter night, at such a time, I watched a man run through the park. There was not another soul in sight, but he ran fast, frantic and silent, as if he were escaping, and I knew he was afraid. Why else would he be running all alone like that at four thirty in the morning? I could feel my scalp come up in wrinkles with sympathetic fear.

This is the hour that a scream can occur. I have heard it three times—twice in a woman's voice, once in a man's. The scream does not last long, but it freezes the blood. It is the scream that every human being holds in reserve but hardly ever has to use, the scream that is the response to sudden mortal threat or unspeakable encounter. Where does it come from? From beyond the Square someplace, but where? To the west? The south? What can it mean? What can I do? The cars continue to speed across the park, to stop for the traffic lights, to move on. No doors fly open, no windows are raised, and the scream is gone, finished. But it existed, and suddenly the empty, spangled park is a place of horror. It is as though a light had been snapped on, and there, in vicious clarity, one had seen the evil that for most of the time lies hidden beneath the immediate events of daily living. Now one knows, with the sharpness of true realization, that one is safe on sufferance at best, that danger is ingenious and always ready.

At these moments, I hate and fear the park, the world, and the possibilities of the future. Even my bed does not seem safe when I return to it. But if I lie awake long enough I will hear the sounds of commencing day—sounds such as I first heard from my crib on distant early mornings. This is the only time of day when one can still hear the clopping of heavy hoofs and the slipshod clatter of wagon wheels. I wonder who uses those big drays now, and for what purpose?

The sky grows lighter by degrees until one can see that it is blue again, though very deep, and only the morning star remains. At six o'clock, there is a chiming from a church nearby. I never have discovered which one. Half an hour later, there's another.

Soon the brooms are sweeping the front steps, the ash cans being thumped against the garbage truck. The baby wakes for good. As I dress him, we look out of the window, and the park is just as it was yesterday and as it will be tomorrow. There are the first dog-walkers and the first cleaning women. They will be followed by the students and the office workers, all in a hurry. At ten o'clock, the mothers and nurses will come into the park, pushing perambulators curved like scallop shells, each one containing a mound of pink or a mound of blue. The waddlers and the strutters also make their first appearance then, and behind them, tinkling or clacking, roll their wheeled possessions. Before long, the park will seethe and gabble in its customary way. Old men will toss old bread crusts to the pigeons, tin spades will turn the musty sand again, the babies will swing like lockets in the playground swings, and evil, or whatever it is that bares its fearful teeth at 4:00 A.M., will once more be hidden decently from view.

The Cradle Janus

Our youngest child was born when his brothers were ten and sixteen years old. All of us, even I, had forgotten exactly what it was like to have a baby in the house and we had forgotten, among other things, about the madcap pace of an infant's development. Nothing was quite the same about him two days running, and looking back on those first months of his life my predominating impression is one of breathless haste and amazement.

In his own way he took over the household with a despotic thoroughness that was nonetheless effective for being unconscious. He had, for instance, not one but three cribs. We lived at the time in a steep little house in a fairly noisy neighborhood; and though beforehand I had planned for him to be a placid, somnolent type of infant, he did not in any way fall in with my design: he was from the first alert, gregarious, and a light sleeper. In those days I was rarely seen without a finger at my lips, hissing for silence. My family wearied of the greeting and after a short period of trial and error it seemed simpler to put the baby to bed on whatever level of the house was quietest at the time, though except at night it was never really still. There was, for one thing, a factory that backed up on the house; a small concern which manufactured luggage and which burst vivaciously into life at eight o'clock each morning with a sound like a concerto for massed cash registers. For this reason a crib in the living room at the front of the house was assigned for the morning nap. . . . Then, early in the afternoon, the garbage trucks came to graze in our street. There were always two of them, one for each side of the street, and one a little behind the other. Like a pair of clangorous water buffaloes they would grind and gorge their leisured way from Sixth Avenue to Fifth, while at their flanks their herdsmen howled and goaded. A crib at the rear of the second floor was reserved for this part of the day; and at night there was still another, on the top floor, well out of range of family mirth and squabble.

In the baby's first weeks the auditory effects were further complicated by the presence of a practical nurse who turned out to be a compulsive talker. Late at night, having talked without stopping all day long, she would linger at my bedside to deliver a last monologue, holding the baby, larva-shaped in his blue blanket, and brandishing him to emphasize her points. I could not wait for her to leave so that I could have him to myself, yet it is humiliating to admit, in the light of psychosomatic theory, that he was first stricken with colic on the day she left.

There followed a stormy month, when every day was a distress for him, until promptly at midnight when he would plummet into sleep and stay there for ten hours. One scene from this era is engraved upon my memory. It is evening and my husband is talking on the telephone; it is a long-distance business conversation and he is annoyed. He holds the receiver in his right hand and growls menacingly into the mouthpiece: "O.K., then, you tell the bastard he knows what he can do! You tell him I said so!" And in his left hand, saddled in his palm and pillowed by the crook of his arm lies the baby, gently held and rocked, asleep for the first time that day.

In view of all the foregoing it is perhaps not remarkable that for a while I became subject to an unusual form of lunacy. I constantly found myself visualizing mature adults as they had been, or might have been, in early infancy. This was not voluntary on my part; it simply occurred. Passing a middle-aged businessman on the street, for example, I would suddenly think: Probably weighed around nine pounds at birth. Ate a lot. Walked late. Rather stolid throughout infancy. Or my eyes would linger on an elderly lady in the bus to the point where she began to twitch, and all the time I would be seeing her as she must have been before the emergence of her first tooth: pink-gummed and guileless.

It is strange that it should be so difficult to imagine adolescence or youth in an aged face; almost as difficult as it is to construct old age upon the faces of the young; and yet to reclaim the mask of infancy—the imagined mask—is all too easy if one is in the proper frame of mind.

I remember indulging in a perfect orgy of this kind one afternoon at a Philharmonic concert. Seated in the dress circle of Carnegie Hall I found it easy and pleasant to reconstruct upon the heads of the musicians—many of them bald—their fontanels; and when the guest artist, a pianist internationally honored, made his first appearance, I at once reduced him to his earliest version: an irascible wine-colored baby with a lot of black hair, beating his heels and fists against the pale-pink lining of his bassinet. (Why pink, I wonder. But pink is how

I saw it.) He would have cut his teeth bitterly, I was sure, balked at his formula, learned to walk early and then been into everything. Probably he would have sucked his thumb.

Fortunately this state of bleary hallucination did not persist; it lasted only a matter of weeks, and I never suffered a relapse.

Time passed. When the boy was three years old—exactly three—he was admitted to nursery school and a kingdom of people all three years old. I also was admitted. Sixteen years before, my eldest child had been taken to school for the first time, kissed briskly, and left to sink or swim. With the second child, six years after *that*, I had lingered for one watchful hour, and departed. But since those days the adjectives "permissive" and "relaxed" had been sounding their didactic tintinnabulations throughout the literature of pediatrics and child psychology. Now it was gently but firmly urged (the whole approach to the parent was now gentle but firm) that the accompanying parent should remain on hand in the group playroom until voluntarily "released" by the offspring. So I remained for seven weeks, as familiar, finally—and as stationary—as a radiator or a blackboard.

The place made me think of a scene from Bedlam as conceived by William Blake. People casually lay down under tables or on top of them; capriciously hurled the clay or tasted the paint; hit each other over the head with blocks, or strolled peacefully in twos, dressed up in ragtags; were suddenly gripped by mass hilarity, or a mass urge to impersonate fire engines. Being three years old, all of them were beautiful.

As I watched them like this, day after day, and came to know them well through observation, another strange thing happened to me; as strange in its way as the delirium that had taken me a few years before when I had revisited their infancy on unsuspecting adults. Observing these three-year-olds, or when I thought of them between times, I found it hard to consider them as children. The prophecy of his maturity seemed implicit in each one; or, rather, the period of his maturity in which, I imagined, his personality would be its most assertive.

Norman, for instance, a dark, bold boy with strong arms and a stentorian voice, I saw distinctly as a man of thirty-five, seated at the wheel of a Cadillac or its future equivalent; and in a premonitory glimpse I caught the worldly glitter of his eye beneath his hatbrim. A gangster, perhaps? No, but very successful in a sharp way. His wife, the first of several, would be a beauty with a durable veneer. His clothes and tastes would be expensive, and whatever adjective of praise was destined to replace "terrific" would be the adjective of praise he used. Objects which merited this word would be the goals of his attainment throughout life.

Serena had an aureole of tiny platinum curls, and eyes as clear as blue glass buttons. She was beautifully dressed, and while the other children emerged at noon grimed and askew, like kobolds from chimneys, Serena's little sweaters stayed pink and white, her hands marvelously clean. There was a quality about her, calm, domestic, which persuaded me that her crowning role in life was to be that of grandmother. She had just those qualities of detachment, solicitude, assurance, which, while perhaps a little too objective for a mother, are among the ornaments of the best grandmothers.

Alec had a withdrawn delicate face; his block towers were precision-built, never subject to exuberant collapse like other people's. He pursed his lips and frowned as he worked, from time to time stepping back quietly to appraise. He never made much noise. To me, he seemed inevitably destined for the law; I saw him in a well-tailored, somber suit, very successful in handling estate cases, possibly, and in his spare time collecting something: Haranobu prints, perhaps, or rare examples of Chinese bronze.

About Kendall there was an air of largeness, a sort of worthy magnificence. All that he built was solid yet original. He was consistent, unswervingly completing whatever he began. His identification with the machine was something to marvel at; he could really become a tractor before your eyes. He could also become a jackhammer, a thunderjet, or a broken-down Ford station wagon, palsied and hiccuping. The pictures he painted, rugged, enormous, and basted with black, looked like the products of a nursery Rouault. Also he knew how to tie a knot. . . . I saw Kendall as a man of fifty against a background of achievements, all large. Suspension bridges? Power plants? Cities? Maybe even governments? His potentialities seemed confined by no mean boundaries.

But for my own son I was unable to see prophecies, just as I was unable to get his likeness when I tried to draw him. I could not imagine him as anything but what he was at the moment; it would have taken someone else to gauge his future, or attempt to. . . . One person who might have, though he never told me if he did, was Peter, the twelve-year-old who sometimes came to help when the teacher was shorthanded.

"I like them when they're three," he said to me. "It's the only time they're ever just the way they really are. When they're four they're kind of getting organized already. Civilized, or something, and you can't see them the same way any more."

I found that what he said was true. At the end of seven weeks I was "released" by my son; and after a few more months the summer came like a wide river between the seasons, and in the fall when we returned to school, I saw the children in a different light. Norman, after all, was not a gangster. He was a little boy whose nose ran, gentler than last year, rather shy; and Serena was no longer an embryonic grandmother but a spirited girl who bossed and boasted and wiped her paint-wet fingers on her overalls. Alec had learned how to make noise, made plenty of it, and was developing a genial social sense; and Kendall, the master builder, gave up sucking his thumb while he painted, and took a robust interest in argument and theory.

Civilization in its complex way was setting in, as Peter had predicted, not so much altering the children as concealing them. Or so it seemed to me. And paradoxically, though many months had passed, and everyone was four years old, and had grown taller, wiser, and more skillful, now in a way they all seemed *younger* than they had at three.

All the Way Back, Please

The crowded bus jolts, stops, jolts forward. With each jolt the packed straphangers lurch in a body and recover like some gross form of rockweed in a current. The handbag of the straphanger at my left knocks my shoulder with pendulum regularity; the thigh of the stranger sitting next to me is pressed so close to mine I might be married to it, but I am lucky to have a seat at all.

Between and around obstacles I am able to catch glimpses of the street where everything today is the same color: sidewalks, stones of buildings, glass store fronts, sky, air, people's faces and clothes, are all different tones of the same blue-gray; it has even invaded the bus; and on the faces of the passengers the expression, like the color of the day, is all the same. It is a dead-serious noncommittal look; a look that would be suitable for many sober purposes: for mastering a minor grief, for preparing to visit a dentist, for reviewing the events leading up to an overdraft, for concern with some personal discomfort such as heartburn or arch trouble. Even the young faces wear this look; it is only more becoming to them, as all things are more becoming to them.

"Step back, step back," orders the driver, and the straphangers push dutifully toward the rear of the bus. The handbag at my shoulder has been replaced by the corner of a cardboard box. I think of the days when no one was allowed to stand in the aisles. It was the war that brought about the stuffing of each bus like a Strasbourg goose, and when it was seen that the public would accept the stuffing, the wartime expedient became the peacetime rule. But I can remember what it was like before the war, and long before it, too.

The old green double-deckers of my youth came down the street like peripatetic bungalows, with roof gardens growing people. On the platform of each a conductor stood as host, leaning forward to give a hoist-up to the fat or laggard. "Take your toim, little lady, take your toim." All the conductors had rich velvety brogues, and faces the color of canned heat.

One remembers individuals among them. There was the gentle abstracted soul who walked the aisle holding out his dime-snatcher and chanting: "Faze, please . . . faze." And there was the comedian standing on the windy platform shouting: "Seats in the dress circle only; aarkestra sold out!"

On spring and summer nights the buses joggled through the town top-heavy with embracers. Kisses at second-story level sped down the lighted avenue; and even without the kissing, riding was a pleasure then. The air, heavy and somehow exciting because of the exhaust fumes, was subtly penetrated by a smell of country—a breath from the parks, and from the few trees that rustled past. When traffic was scarce and the bus bowled along briskly there was a feeling of reckless speed, a rocking and jouncing that seemed to belong more to a vessel in choppy waters than to a motored vehicle. Store windows went by in glares of merchandise, all the more dazzling and tempting because seen at a dash, and overhead, belittled by city lights, one could spy a few seedy stars if one wished. "There's the Little Dipper up there," I once heard a man say as he pointed to Cassiopeia's Chair, and then pointing to the Northern Crown he said: "And there's what they call the Plee-ads." The girl looped in his arm gave them the attention she might have given the Bronxville Station seen from a train window.

Nearing one's destination one rang a loud doorbell that was set in the railing; and then began the truly perilous departure from the bus, first reeling along the aisle to the bucking stair and there clinging to the rail with the clutch of a kinkajou as the wind blew water out of one's eyes. Leaving the platform one caught a glimpse of the interior bus riders seated decently, like churchgoers, and no one standing in the aisle but the conductor.

But now it is different. The crowded bus smells strongly of cloth and human endurance. All the passengers seem to be strangers to one another; at least there is no conversation. The only sounds are those made by money ringing in the fare box, doors opening and closing, straphangers shuffling.

No one helps the fat or laggard now. "Step up, step up," orders the driver, not favoring them with a glance, and up they step in fear of the gnashing doors as fast as pounds, years, packages will let them. "Step back, step back," commands the driver, still not satisfied. "*All* the way back!"

Traffic is heavy today. We have been a long time on our way. There is a mole on the neck of a man in front of me which has become my friend, at least I feel I've known it a lifetime. I am also very familiar with his ears and his hairline, and with the hood of the woman sitting next to him. It is a red hood with two tails like Tyl Eulenspiegel's, and it is decorated, for some reason, with real pennies. When she turns her head for a moment and I see her face I wonder what ever made this woman choose a jester's cap? Her profile looks as noble and decisive as that of Thomas Jefferson.

Jolt, stop, jolt forward. How long has this been going on? Time itself is running down.

Somewhere at this moment people are sitting on a terrace above the sea, cracking crab claws and drinking wine, with nothing to bother them but the flies.

Somewhere in some ocean at this moment, a swimmer hangs in a blue element above a bed of sea anemones colored like the dahlias at a country fair.

And at this moment, in the desert, the huge barbed sahuaros are putting out their frugal flowers, and the ocotillo is tagged with red firecracker papers. In that place the noon sun presses down like the flat of a hand, harder, harder, harder. It is so still that one can almost hear the panting of the lizard on the rock, and the faraway mountains are transparent; one can see the sky through them.

At these thoughts the spirit in me gives a leap and a howl like a dog shut up in a basement for too long; but I know that my face is as serious and noncommittal as those of my fellow passengers; and I wonder how many dogs of spirits are howling in this bus?

The Same Music

When I went to France last summer it was for the first time since I was eighteen years old. I had lived there at that age for nearly a year: a green American girl, typical of the day, wearing very short skirts, spike heels, a brassière so tight it made me cough, and a hat that swept down over my brow and ears like the headdress of a paltry sphinx. My belt was poised somewhere between my hips and knees, and my pale beige stockings were made of silk or lisle because nylon had not been invented yet. Think of it: no nylon, no Ban-Lon, no Dacron, no Acrilan; and more than that, no Kleenex, no frozen spinach, no instant anything. It seems an era as remote in time as that of the bustle and the four-in-hand—more remote, in a way, because constant drastic change creates an illusion of time enormously elapsed.

Still, certain things remain the same no matter how they're draped. Today's girl, with her long curtains of hair hanging into her eyes, into her food, pressed, blowing against her whitened lips, with her large frank toes at play on the soles of her thong sandals, and her darkened eyelids making two black buttonholes in her face ("buttonholes" reminds me: there were no zippers, either. Good God!)—today's girl, Lorelei with her skirts cropped, remains in many ways the same as her grandmother: that militant virgin with the straight-front shirt-waist, narrow belt, surging behind, and goiterous forward-thrusting pompadour; she is the same as I was in my own cropped skirts. Different in manner, and manners, in use of language, in morals, no doubt, but there we all are, were, and will be, in the similarity of being young. We bear a family resemblance from generation to generation in the way we whoop, whisper, giggle, connive and confide, fall prey to in-teresting melancholies, are constantly establishing precedents, all of which have been established before, but never by us; in the way we know that we are right and that because our life is long before us, and probably infinite, we can take time for anything and yet are in a hurry. We are alike in the way we can fall in love, with people, places, ideas, words, music, horses, dogs, and cats, with modes of thought and modes of dress.

It was a place I fell in love with first, and the place was Paris. I was taken there as a child of thirteen after a sojourn in Holland with my mother: two weeks of rain or mirthless pewter skies, of dank canals where people emptied chamber pots, of no heat in the hotels because it was supposed to be June. The tulips were gone. The rosy faces of burghers on museum walls, the glowingly painted dresses of their *vruows*, were the warmest things we saw. And we knew no one; no one to be strangers with.

In Paris on the first day the sun came out. We met friends.

The horse chestnuts sailed boats of flowers; the children in the park wore little gloves and shook hands with each other. It was like no other city I had known, noisy in a more cheerful way, and it smelled of perfume. For lunch there were tiny things like grasshoppers to eat, delicious, and *fraises des bois* with *petits suisses*. In the afternoon we all took a carriage up the Champs Elysées into the Bois to Armenonville or some such place, where we sat outdoors next to the dance floor and ate ices. At least I did. There were mirrors and geraniums, the sky was pure blue, the horse chestnuts loomed in mountains. One of my mother's friends, an Englishman, led me out onto the dance floor though I could not dance yet, only stagger and lean. He clasped me firmly and dragged me along to the music, a handkerchief pressed delicately between my palm and his. The orchestra couldn't drown the song of chaffinches. Before I knew it I was in love—not with the Englishman, indeed, but with the city.

When we returned a few years later it was the same. Paris was a gray city then; it lay like proud gray lions along the Seine, but its noise was the noise of macaws and peacocks and blue jays and geese. Late at night in my bedroom above a quiet garden I could hear the distant avian squawks of traffic from all the boulevards in Paris; now and then they would be dimmed a little by the sound of wind stirring in the garden below. There was a stand of bamboo there—dry, papery in the fall and winter. The wind stirred those rustling leaves first before it rose and breathed among the branches. It sounded lonely, a wanderer from a far time and place. I would shiver in my bed, happy, cozy, safe from the sadness I heard in the night wind. Morning would come. The Seine would be a blinding yellow, and the mists yellow, and the plane leaves yellow; I would go to the cab rank near St. François Xavier, climb into a high old *peau rouge* taxi driven by an enthroned walrus, and off we would travel through all that topaz light, all that yellow, almost gold, to the art school in the shadows of the Place des Vosges.

I welcomed each day.

This time, coming back, another person with another life, I found the city turned to cream; at night really to gold. I was not sure I did not like it better gray, though I knew it was more beautiful this way. The traffic was different, too. I remembered those *peau rouge* taxis, square and commodious; great camions as high as barns; cart horses with fetlocks draped about their hoofs as if their stockings had fallen down. I remembered the overbearing snouts of wealthy cars; the Minerva, for instance, which wore the goddess as a radiator cap; the arklike hood of the Rolls-Royce with its perpetually chilly figure; the Hispano Suiza flying a bird—a swan?—a falcon?— surely not a goose? And then the small fry, small in phrase only: Citroëns, Peugeots, Renaults, and the rest; all of them long, large, and loud. All of them gone. Now the cars were little; they swarmed through the streets by the thousand, like piranhas, deadly, swift, and, above all, silent. No more squawks. It was as well, perhaps, that now there were signs that flashed for the pedestrians: *piétons;* and the pedestrians obeyed. In the old days one commended one's soul to the Lord, looked right, looked left, and drawing a deep breath, plunged. Sometimes a gendarme in his pirouetting cape came to the rescue, raising his baton as if to start the music.

The river traffic was as I remembered it. My hotel window, wide, and wide open, with a box of obstinate geraniums on the sill, looked out across the Seine to tilted trees and the majestic ramparts of the Louvre. I watched the barges going by: domestic scenes of housewives sweeping the decks of their water houses, sweeping and traveling at the same time, hanging up the wash, or swatting their children absent-mindedly while their dogs barked at the passing world. Between the nearest trees and our narrow pavement the small, fierce, quiet cars made another river.

Each day I walked the marvelous city; some days with my children, some days alone. Besides the glories of creamy stone, of jeweled Notre Dame, of the freighted river with its bridges, the leaf-freighted trees in the parks, I remember the details that charmed me: too many to describe . . . only a few . . .

For instance there was an *alimentation* with open windows in which were set out trays of small Charentais melons, raspberries, early peaches, all exuding a smell so heavenly, so heady, it was better than the taste could ever be. I walked to and fro beside it several times, breathing in gustily. It is nearly impossible to remember a smell; but I can almost remember that one.

There was a priest on a motor bike, his skirts flying. He looked like a sort of witchy suffragette, except that he was smiling. There were four nuns packed into a *deux cheveaux*, like hens on the way to market.

There were the poplars on the river bank. I heard their rustling and thought instantly of the times when I used to drive out to the countryside at night with a boy I knew. From time to time we would stop under other poplars, tall roadside trees, hissing overhead between us and the beady stars; we would stop to kiss and touch, every sense inquisitive, exploring, virginity narrowly preserved, *but* preserved, as it so often was in that far day.

There was a dog in an open window—some sort of large spaniel with a long nose, long ears, and what looked like a curled toupee on his brow. As he leaned out between flowerpots, one paw posed on the sill and his ears clapping as he admonished the passer-by with deep authoritarian barks, he reminded one of an English judge in a court of law impersonating a dog.

The other dogs, too. The ubiquitous fox terrier—where had

he (or probably she) been all these years but in France, getting smaller, shrewder, and fatter? And those casual, casually bred dogs, large, scruffy, and benevolent that lay trustfully asleep in gutter or on doorstep, flapping a napping tail at a kind word.

And the cats with French faces: pert midinette faces, and tough fur. The birds croaking or warbling in little cages. The exuberant flowers bunched in stalls. A thousand things. As I walked I was hardly a person at all; only an instrument for seeing, hearing, smelling.

But there were changes, I discovered, besides the color of the buildings and the shape of the traffic. The lifted-oar trees of the Île St. Louis had disappeared from the bank opposite the Quai de la Tournelle; new trees, young and stiff, replaced them, though those on the other side of the island remained the same. The art school on the Place des Vosges had closed long ago. "Yes," said the man in an art gallery there, "I've heard there *was* a school here once. . . ." And though nearly all the restaurants I had known still lived their robust lives, the one we'd loved the best of all, on the Place Beauvau, had given up the ghost.

On the fourth day in Paris I went, alone, on a pilgrimage to the short street where I had lived as a student. I went secretly, avidly, with some trepidation, walking across the Pont Alexandre III, past the Invalides, along the boulevard, past the church of St. François Xavier to the Rue de Babylone, where I turned left. It gave me heart to see that the Chinese Legation still stood on its walled corner, the familiar green ceramic roof with all its snouts and tilted eaves showing among waterfalls of weeping beech: a stout, gay, grim building, just as I remembered. Chinese no longer, legation no longer, it was now a cinema. Still it was *there*, looking almost exactly as it had, and I went by it encouraged toward the street I once had known by heart.

When I came to it I was happy to see that it looked very

much the same, bathed though it was in the acid, truthful light of half past two in the afternoon. Some of the houses that I recognized had rearranged their positions in my mind, and now took up their rightful places. Some were shabbier. One that I remembered had a cornice adorned with the busts of philosophers. Someone, sometime, had painted them yellow, and the paint was peeling from their chins and noses, as if they were recovering from scarlet fever. There was the building which had housed a convent of cloistered nuns. It looked closed and secret and I wondered if they still were there; we used to see the long bread being brought in baskets and thrust into a small opening let into the locked door: invisible hands would draw it in. There was a house not far from ours that was wrapped in vines, and it still was. The windows on the second floor stood open; most, on this hot afternoon, were closed or shuttered. . . .

Our apartment, toward the far end of the street, had been on the second floor of a five-story, eighteenth-century building, U-shaped around a court. I could feel my heart accelerating foolishly as I approached the spot.

But all was changed. I saw that before I reached it. On the site of our old building, with its footstep-clacking court, its tubs of laurel, its heterogeneous occupants, its quarreling cats, its sighing garden, there was now a different apartment house which already looked of a respectable age.

Perhaps I had made a mistake? Perhaps farther on? But I knew I had made no mistake, and suddenly felt much older than I was; infinitely removed from a valued era. I felt as if I should be dressed in black, warped sideways with arthritis, thinking elderly thoughts (if one ever does), creeping agedly along that traitorous street. As I turned about to go back—it was not a thought so much as a feeling—I was aware of an impression, or memory, of the night wind I used to hear long ago in the garden below my window.

Still, I was in Paris, there was everything to see and no real reason to be despondent (except that there was every reason to be despondent) and I noticed without caring that someone was playing a piano: dreary at that time of day. There were some chords; an arpeggio and then another—they issued from the open windows of the vine-bound house. Something stirred in my mind; I stopped and looked up. The arpeggios dawdled and ceased. There was a pause. And then with a gallop and flair the player dashed into a piece of music with the confidence of long usage.

I put my hand against the wall, not for support, but to touch something real and hard. The tune that bounded from the second floor was "La Lisonjera," by Cécile Chaminade, a nearly forgotten composer; nearly forgotten in my day, even. "Trivial," my Aunt Lucile Watson had said, as her diamonds flashed over the keyboard. "Trivial and showy. Circus spangles. That's why I like it." But when I first listened to my Aunt Lucile play it I was already familiar with the piece, having heard it many, many times already issuing from these very windows. I remember on summer afternoons and evenings wishing that she (it must be a she, I thought) would for goodness' sake play something else. She did, of course, but this one seemed to be her favorite, returned to over and over and over again. I heard it so often that when I was away it galloped in my ear against my will.

I was glad to hear it now—I can never say how glad. Was the music a little slower? But if the player was the same—and I would not consider anything else—her fingers were more than thirty-five years older.

I listened to the piece until it ended and then, when, after another little pause, she began to play the sweetish strains of Satie's "Gnossienne," I went on my way. I could not remember that I had ever heard that music coming from those open windows, and then it occurred to me that in that day, it, like Acrilan, had perhaps not yet been invented.

The music, I found, had made a spell for me. The black, the creeping, the arthritis, all were lifted from my mood. Because of that music, the same music heard in the same place half a lifetime later, I felt at peace: safe in a continuum forever. That was false, I knew. Someday the playing and the player would stop for good, and someday I would, too. Still, I only knew this, I did not believe it.

As I walked the city all that day and the days following, I saw that so much of what I had known in early youth was exactly as I remembered it—the yellow light of morning, the street lamps and their shadows at night, a thousand things— there was no film of habitude between me and what I saw; the years between our confrontation were no years at all. Walking and walking, I was happy in a way I had forgotten, and in everything but tawdry fact was young again.

Stories

The Stroke of Twelve

The cathedral stood in a windy town; large, clumsy, and magnificent. Being made of native stone which was rich in iron, it was a somber color; the color of dried blood. It could be seen as a pair of blunted steeples miles before one reached the town: it sailed, obstinate, unhurried, a ship of stone, rising and falling to different perspectives, until, finally, growing, becoming a fact, one arrived at its roots in the windy plaza.

Charlotte Henry, a single woman in her forties, got out of her rented Peugeot, a little stiffly. She had been driving for hours. Her binoculars clapped at her ribs in the wind. In one hand she held her guidebook, in the other her handbag. She held onto that bag firmly, consciously, all the time. Since it contained her passport, her money, her tickets, her traveler's checks, two letters of value—one from her closest friend, and

one from the married man who had been her lover for years—
she felt it was her own life she carried, certainly her own
identity: therefore precious, out of all proportion in this foreign country where she spoke the language with difficulty,
and had no friends. If she should lose that bag she would be
lost herself, she felt.

Never again, she vowed, would she travel alone in a strange
country. She had had enough of lying awake at night in hotel
bedrooms listening to unfamiliar sounds. Nothing so under-
lines loneliness, so bespeaks indifference, as the audible evidence of lives and activities which can in no way concern one's
self; she had had enough of eating in restaurants, a *dame seule*,
looking down at her plate discreetly, pretending to be comfortable, pretending to be at ease. But since she was here, she
was determined to look at things she had wanted to see for
years—this cathedral was one—and perhaps later, remembering
them, she could enjoy them.

At first she was disappointed: the huge building seemed
crude, and she found the color ponderous and overbearing.
Pressed against the dark-blood stones, seamed in the crevices,
ferns and plants had taken root—a fur of white stonecrop
growing on crimson stems, mosses, a cluster of valerian, tufts
of yellowed grass—the cathedral was hoary, inappropriately
haired as an old face. Dust skirled around her legs, a torn
newspaper clung desperately to her ankle and she kicked it
away.

Then she heard a medieval sound of jackdaws: a sort of
mewing twang in the air. She looked up to see them, and saw
the gargoyles.

There were dozens of them, scores of them. Some, the rain-
spouts, were smaller than the others. Some were perched about
the eaves for—what? Ornament? Derision? To ward off evil
with their evil faces? They were not human monsters, not
devils, but beasts: morbid dragons, lizards, pterodactyls, de-

formed frogs. Some bent their necks toward one another in frozen, hideous antagonism, and all their mouths, beaks, snouts, jaws, were wide open in a yell of silence.

Charlotte walked slowly around the cathedral, staring up, till her neck hurt, at the savage carvings. There were no twins, each one was different, though all were obviously members of a family. She had never seen anything to touch them. Beautifully made, arrested forever in a tranced violence, they caused her to feel awe; as if she experienced something of the thinking, of the superstitions of the medieval mind. As if that mind were her own, and had always been.

When she went into the cathedral it was deathly cold, and smelled of all its centuries. A nun knelt before a dressy figure of the Virgin. To her left the votive candle flames dipped together, pointed: a bed of burning tulips. Charlotte envied the nun her heavy skirts, her shawl, wimple, and veil, even her stout shoes, all warm.

Somewhere in the church a man blew his nose, and the vaulted stone magnified and dignified the homely noise: an echo of Gabriel's trump. Across the nave someone spoke softly to someone else; also magnified, the voice sounded cool, mysterious—the impersonal voice of an angel.

Charlotte was not a Catholic. She was not sure whether she believed in God or not, but thought probably not. Still it could do no harm (even if it was only superstition, it could do no harm) to say a prayer.

Kneeling, and it hurt her knees to do it, she put her forehead against her hands. But instead of trust she felt her familiar fear—the fear that had sent her on this trip to France, and that lay inside her mind ready to wake up a thousand times a day. . . . Her lover's edginess, lately, his periodic remoteness . . . A husband after years can have his edginess and his remoteness, but he will probably stay married. Whereas a lover . . . And an anxious woman is her own worst enemy.

"Let it be all right," Charlotte prayed. To lose love at this age . . . at any age terrible, but at this age worse. "Let it only be my imagining. . . ."

She tried to erase the fear; at least for the moment to lose herself in the peace of supplication—of honest supplication, not just the whimpering reiteration of her doubts, but she could not. She stood up, shivering with cold. Her binoculars banged against the pew, producing echoed bangs. The nun turned a calm face to look at her, and she tiptoed out.

The hotel was at the edge of the *place*, and her windows looked out at the cathedral. It was a comfortable, stuffy room with large dark furniture and a patterned rug. For one night it would be her house. She changed her dress, hung up her suit and dressing gown in the large brooding *armoire;* at seven she went downstairs to the dining room.

It was a commercial hotel; the room was full of men—just outside, in the lobby, she had noticed a candid row of hand-basins, towels hanging on a rack, and balls of yellow soap on prongs. But where men eat, the food is apt to be good, she knew. And it was; beginning with a hearty soup flavored with dill, and going on to *langoustines* and a green salad. The *langoustines* looked at her pleadingly from their dish, with large, grave eyes, but she ate them, every one, and sucked the morsels from their tails and claws. She had ordered a bottle of wine—a Meursault—and it warmed her. She had come to rely on wine. It made her a companion to herself, instead of a stranger to be doubted. She drank deeply, and the color came into her cheeks, the looks to her face. A man at the next table, industriously cleaning his teeth, smiled at her winningly above the toothpick. She looked down at her plate and did not look up again.

But after dinner he was waiting for her in the lobby. He was not a bad-looking man: merry, dark, about her own age.

"Madame would care to take a little walk?"

Well, she was lonely and had had a lot of wine.

"A very little walk, then."

Outside the air was still, the wind gone. The cathedral lifted its great shoulders against a starry sky.

She and the man talked; he came from Lyons and was a salesman. At the outskirts of the *place*, in a dark alleyway, he took her in his arms and kissed her. His breath smelled faintly of garlic and a hint of perfume. Sen-Sen? Or the French equivalent? But when she found herself responding, she broke away.

"No, no. Oh, no, I'm sorry."

He was a decent man and let her go. Her nervous footsteps rattled across the cobbled *place*.

Disturbed, the wine still humming in her head, she let herself into her hotel room, bolted the door, and went to bed. She read for a long time, and finally beginning to feel drowsy, moved cautiously, gently, so as not to break the spell, and turned out the light.

Oh, no, you don't! It's not so easy! Sleep said to her, as it often did; and she was wide awake. For a time she lay where she was, waiting patiently for drowsiness to come again, but when it did not, she turned on the light, got up and took a sleeping pill. After a while, after a long while, during which she steadfastly refused to review her fear, she began to experience the vague, warm intimations of sleep.

The cathedral clock struck twelve. She had heard too many of its statements already: first nine, then ten, then eleven; each spaced note lingering on the air until the next one. If smoke could have a voice it would be like that, she had thought: that lingering of sound between two sounds.

Twelve takes a long time to ring itself; before the last note she was wakeful again, and conscious of still another sound— no, sounds—several of them at once that she was unable to identify: a sort of nickering and mewing, uncertain and sporadic.

At first she thought it was the jackdaws—but at this hour? And then the noises changed, gave way to hoarse croakings, louder and louder, and without feeling, like a chorus of mechanical dogs. Charlotte felt the hair rise on her nape (and in some far, objective corner of her mind took note of this). She sat up, shivering, and put her cold feet out of bed. Now, to the din of croakings were added other sounds—voices?— that were dry, staccato, repetitious, and harsh, reminiscent of castanets, or the parched racketing of the cicadas she had heard in Provence.

She walked on her bare feet to the window, drew aside the curtain and looked out.

An old moon had risen in the sky. It gave enough light to show her the gargoyles on their roosts and perches; all with their mouths wide open.

It could not be. It could not be. Charlotte looked wildly at the empty street below, the empty *place*. There was not a soul in sight. She waited for people to rush from their houses, for lights to go on, windows to be thrown open, for public awe or consternation in the face of this stupendous utterance.

No doors flew open, no windows sprang into light. The obdurate reptilian chorus continued and now, incongruously, was joined by sounds of piping sweetness, of silver bells, of hylas in spring marshes, cold as ice.

She did not know what to do, was literally paralyzed and stood there in the open window, staring at the motionless stone monsters and listening to their voices: the harsh and barking fabric of their noise, shot through and through with icy threads of silver.

And then it stopped; stopped dead, as though sliced off, and her ears rang with the silence. Across the *place* a man went walking, whistling to himself, hands in his pockets, safe in his true world, matter-of-fact. Bitterly, bitterly, Charlotte wished she were that man.

When she got into her bed again she was frozen, shuddering, at a loss. After a long time the drug, mercifully, began to work, and she fell asleep.

When she woke in the morning, roused by the bells for early Mass—it was a Sunday—the thing came back to her. But after her *petit déjeuner*, after the strong, sensible coffee, she was nearly able to persuade herself: it was the wine, too much wine, and the barbiturate. Together they had forced on her the dream, or fantasy—she had read of such things happening, and would be more careful in the future. But she was anxious to get away, never to think of the place if she could help it, and by a quarter to eight was in the lobby paying her bill.

The bells were ringing again when she went out; the *place* and the street were full of people on their way to eight o'clock Mass: people of all ages, children, crones, whole families dressed in black. Why? She wondered. Mourning? Custom? Economy? They streamed past her toward the open doors.

A young porter brought out her dressing case and put it in the trunk of the car. She tossed her binoculars, bag, gloves, guidebook onto the front seat, and stepped away for a last look at the gargoyles. There was nothing to alarm her now. The beasts were disarmed: grotesque architectural toys, nothing worse . . . someone's childhood nightmares worked out in stone.

"Madame admires our menagerie?" the porter said, following the direction of her glance.

He was very handsome, young, assured. Looking at him she was able, in less than a second, as one is, to wonder if he was married, to speculate on his most intimate life: was he kind or cruel, wise or dull? Then she returned her attention to the gargoyles.

"They look as if they were shouting . . . as if they should be making sounds of some sort, don't they?"

"Ah, Madame, they do. It's said they do; but only once a year, and then only to one person—and for him it is bad luck. He never lives to hear them twice. . . . Of course, it's superstition; I don't believe it, but my grandmother did, she claimed she'd known a man who heard them." He laughed, and crossed himself carelessly. "I never have, thank God."

"Thank God," Charlotte repeated, not hearing herself. The sky was full of lemon light, but the cathedral was so high it held the sun behind it. She stared up at the monsters in their attitudes of howl and croak; jackdaws flew in whinnying flocks, disturbed by the clanging bells. People hurried past into the dark maw of the building. The bells stopped; she heard the stately groaning of an organ. Groaning and groaning; and then the groaning chants of Latin. The fear she had carried in her thoughts for months seemed all at once inconsequential, a child of fears compared to the one that now began to dominate her mind.

The young man cleared his throat. He was still beside her, waiting. Waiting for his tip, of course.

"*Je vous demande pardon, Monsieur,*" Charlotte said. "*Un moment . . .*"

She turned automatically to the car to get her purse. She would give him his money, get the keys out of her bag, and start her journey. There was nothing else for her to do. She opened the car door and leaned in. There on the seat were her binoculars, her book, her gloves. But the bag was gone.

An Hour in September

Summer was over in twenty minutes that day. Finished. At four o'clock in the afternoon the roses were quiet on their stems, full-blown, fulfilled; the water in the pool was warm; the leaves on the trees quiet, too, and green. The cat lay with his belly to the sun, steeped in heat.

We saw the white band of the cold front in the sky. It moved rapidly, like a huge sickle, and when it reached us it was as though we had been cut. We were cut. The wind fell on us, shrieking; petals spattered from the roses, the pool was roughened and roiled, the trees all bent in the same direction, toward the east. The cat roused up, gave his fur an angry lick and trotted to the house.

By half past four the wind had gone, and so had the great black cloud the sickle had tugged behind it. The sky was blue again, but an icy Scandinavian blue. The roses, except for their tight buds, were finished, only a haggard petal clinging here and there. The pool was full of leaves, and those still on the trees were all ruffed up, showing their gray undersides.

Summer was gone; there would not be another for a year. Nearly a year.

"It should never be so quick," I said to my husband. "Autumn should come on slowly. It should overtake in a leisurely manner, not pounce like a dog on a bone."

"Yup," said my husband, who had not heard a word. He seldom heard my words, having developed that connubial deafness familiar to wives of long standing.

"Next thing it will be storm windows."

I thought of many an autumn I had known: seemly autumns approaching deliberately, with amplitude. I thought of wild asters, Michaelmas daisies, mushrooms, leaves idling down the air, two or three at a time, warblers twittering and glittering in every bush ("Confusing fall warblers," Peterson calls them, and how right he is); the lingering yellow jackets feeding on broken apples; crickets; amber-dappled light; great geese barking down from the north; the seesaw noise that blue jays seem to make more often in the fall. Hoarfrost in the morning, cold stars at night. But slow; the whole thing coming slowly. The way it should be.

"Storm windows, winter coats," I said. "Oh, hell. Summer is the wink of an eye, and winter is forever."

"Yup," my husband replied and, whistling, went to the garage to get the leaf rake and the wheelbarrow.

I was cold; the air was really chilly, now, and I went into the house, turned up the thermostat and made myself a cup of tea. The cat followed me into the kitchen, purring, wafting, rubbing; from time to time he opened his thorny pink mouth and meowed silently; too lazy to make the sound—only the grimace.

"Parasite," I said to him, and gave him a bowl of milk.

We drank together, he and I. He lip-lipped quietly, now and then waving his tail, now and then looking up, abrupt and concentrated, at the kind of ghost cats seem to see.

I drank my painful tea, too impatient to let it cool; its little steam floated between my eyes and the window. Through it I could see my husband, tall, middle-aged, but still moving with the loping grace of an athlete; distinguished-looking, patient, a good man. I sighed.

"Well, I'll go up to the attic and get out the winter coats," I said to the cat. If I had had no cat I would have said it out loud to myself. I often catch myself doing that, but so far only when I'm alone, thank God. In old age I'll probably be one of those crones who toddle along the streets talking animatedly or indignantly to no one, and laughing at interior jokes.

"I'll bring them down," I said. "Then tomorrow I can hang them on the line and get the moth-stuff smell out of them."

So I did that. I went up to the attic where the large bags were hanging on the rack, as they had been since spring, among others that had been there longer. The attic was like many attics, tidier than the rest of the house: luggage stacked neatly, boxes stacked neatly, beach hats on hooks spread flat as sunflowers against the wall. Winter boots, galoshes, waders in empty, lonesome pairs beside the trunks. Fishing tackle. Tennis rackets. The place was full of mementoes: the beach hats, summer dresses; toys outgrown, but too good to throw away, waiting for phantom grandchildren of the future. All Ted's model planes were there, neatly hangared on a shelf, his old space helmet and cloak, and Glory's patient dolls; patient and bored to tears, they looked. I picked one up and pressed its plastic cheek to mine. Nothing; a door knob. I thought of the time last year when Ted, fourteen, home for spring vacation, had gone vigorously to work at putting away childish things: that's why the planes were here, the books he had loved and thought himself too old for, the ray guns, puzzles, and the rest.

The children were dedicatedly shedding their childhood; but as children they had lived with us for a short time before departing, and we would not forget them.

The cat boxed at a spider in the window. I opened the first bag and took out my heavy coats, fusty-smelling, too familiar. In the next one I found the children's parkas all outgrown; why had I saved them? I took them out to give away, and behind them was my husband's jacket from Austria. I had almost forgotten about that jacket; he hadn't worn it in several years, having grown too heavy for it. Perhaps it would do for Ted. I lifted it out, sniffed at the camphory wool, felt in the pockets. I always do that; once I found a twenty-dollar bill. In the outer pockets there were only ticket stubs, a paper clip, one penny; but in the inside pocket there was a letter without its envelope.

The handwriting gave me a jolt. I knew it better than my own though it was a long time since I'd seen it. I thought of that friend, my best friend, Nora. I've never laughed as I laughed with her; I never admitted so much as I admitted to her; we were as comfortable to each other as old shoes, but unlike old shoes not dull or shabby. She was a witty one, a pretty one, but best of all she was interesting; a companion. It should never have happened to her, of all people; the bleaching and shrinking; the listening look that people have who are in chronic pain. Oh, no, it should not have happened to her, she should have lived forever! The only thing one can say about it is that it was quick; some people linger on for years with hope in one hand and terror in the other.

"Darling," the letter began—well, I thought it was meant for me, that I'd forgotten it—she sometimes used that endearment to me, though it was an extravagant way for her to start a letter—but after the first sentence I knew it was not meant for me. "Darling," it said. "You left your lighter, did you miss it? I found it when I moved the bed. Last time it was your tie clasp, and in the spring that terrible umbrella. I'm glad. They say when people leave things behind they love the place they're leaving. . . ."

That's the way it went; I read it all. It was only a note, really. Then I read it again. It was undated; Thursday was all it said; but Nora's house had been the graveyard for more than two years, and before that she had been sick—so it was old.

I had three impulses: the first one was to kick the cat; the next to knock my head against the wall; the next to storm downstairs and out of doors to confront my husband with the letter. I did none of those things. I stood where I was remembering things I had not known I noticed. I stood there trying to regain my balance like someone who is drunk, or standing on a pitching deck. Everything I saw was changed, was different, even the galoshes and the toys. After a while I tore the letter into bits and put them in my pocket. When I went downstairs I would drop them into the garbage pail outside the kitchen door and nobody would ever know about it. Then, if I could keep my mouth shut . . .

If I could keep my mouth shut we would live, he and I; pay our bills, finish educating our expensive children, criticize or praise our mutual friends (our mutual friends!), eat our meals together, sleep together, make love together, sometimes . . . travel . . . work . . . If I could keep my mouth shut.

I went to the window and looked down from the attic at the stranger raking up leaves, whistling cheerfully as he worked; contented. There were thousands of leaves, it would take him a long time, and thousands more were waiting in the trees: they looked dry and still disheveled. The dahlias, garroted by wind, hung their ponderous ruined heads, and fallen apples paved the ground beneath the apple tree. I knew it was not only the summer that was gone. Gone was the word, and **gone forever.**

I Pine for Thee

Mrs. Thorpe, a hundred years old, sat in the high-backed Renaissance chair with a balsam pillow at the small of her back, an old-fashioned eared hassock under her feet, and flashbulbs popping in her face; she hardly blinked at them; her eyes, like agates, stared impassive from a labyrinth of wrinkles.

One of the photographers crept up and crouched before her, aiming at her. "How about a nice big smile, honey?"

The agates turned slowly in his direction and fixed themselves on him; the narrow mouth winced slightly at one corner. It could hardly be called a smile.

The room was crowded but not smoky; no one was allowed to smoke. There were many offerings of September flowers: large brandishings of gladioli, and blowsy dahlia heads already beginning to sag. The cake with its hundred candles had been lighted, photographed—she with it, knife gripped in a canary claw—and blown out for safety's sake. The time had not yet come to eat it.

She had answered the questions about her ancient past and added the bits of information that people seemed to find impressive. Yes, she remembered the Indians coming to her grandfather's house in wintertime, bringing venison or pheasants in exchange for a bucket of live coals. Yes, she remembered meeting Ralph Waldo Emerson in her childhood. He had laid his hand on her head. Her eyes having been on a level with his watch chain it was really only the watch chain that she remembered. But she did have a clear recollection of being lifted up to see President Lincoln go by in a carriage; she had never forgotten that sad sallow face beneath the towering hat.

Yes, she had known Eleanora Duse; entertained her right in this very house. "Picture's over there," she said, motioning toward the piano, heavily freighted with photographs. Yes, she had lived in this house ever since her marriage, though it was only a little house then; prosperity and an increasing family had caused them to add on and on to it. Children? They had once had four, but three had died in the same month of scarlet fever.

"Children died like flies in those days," she said carelessly. "Only Addie was left. Addie was the baby."

The young reporters glanced for a moment at Addie, a woman of seventy-two, who could never have been a baby.

"Are you warm enough, Mother? Are you comfortable?"

"Yes, I'm warm enough, but I'm not comfortable. I haven't been comfortable since I was eighty!"

Mrs. Thorpe often said this. It was good for some sort of laugh.

One of the reporters asked the standard question: "Ma'am, could you tell us what you attribute your long life to? To what you attribute it, I mean?"

"Enough money," Mrs. Thorpe said.

"Oh, now, Mother, what an answer!" Addie turned to the reporters. "My mother's life has been full of interests, *that's* what's kept her going. Friends—well, you should see the cards—friends all over! She was president of the garden club until ten years ago—she still takes great interest in her flowers. She loves to listen to the Talking Book records and she's very fond of music, she used to be a highly accomplished—"

"It's the money," Mrs. Thorpe said. "If you're rich, people talk to you. Pay attention to you. Old women in poor circumstances die from lack of conversation as much as anything; lack of attention. But everyone is nice to money."

"Honestly, she's the limit," Addie's daughter Helen, forty-eight, whispered to her own daughter, Deirdre, twenty-two. "She's acting like some old woman in a play; as though she'd rehearsed it for a month—"

"Oh, Great-granny's always been a character," Deirdre said, absently. At the moment she was not interested in her great-grandmother. Being in love, she was interested only in love, the object of which lurked in the background watching her and wishing he could smoke.

"Well, Deirdre, I'm not so sure. It seems to me she only started being a character about twenty years ago. Just about the time my father died and Mother moved back here to live. Before that she was—she just seemed rather old and normal. I liked her when I was little. Except she was forever combing my hair and braiding it and trying to read the Bible to me."

"Great-*granny?* I thought she always was a heathen."

"She started being one about the time she started being a character. One day—I was there, I heard it—she just banged her Bible shut and said 'I'm tired of this book, it doesn't really tell you much.' And she said the Old Testament was nothing but riddles and gossip, and she had the New by heart anyway, so she didn't need to read it ever again, and as far as I know she never has."

"You know, Mummy, I'm so glad he's tall," Deirdre said. "I'd hate to marry a man who was shorter than me."

"Oh, Deirdre. Than I. And you haven't listened to a word."

"Yes, I have. I think it shows great perspicacity and independence on her part. I mean abandoning the Bible at an age when most people are latching onto it like mad. But really, Mummy, aren't you glad he's taller than me? Than I?"

"Yes, dear, you look wonderful together."

Agnes and Bridie, the maids who had been with Mrs. Thorpe for forty years, now came into the room with trays of punch cups. Slowly they crept from group to group, bringing with them a faint smell of dryness and service.

Mrs. Thorpe, given the first cup, grasped it in her two hands to steady it; her rings clicked sideways on her knuckles. There was the sudden ringing of a spoon, then silence. What was going to happen now?

Helen's husband, a florid, genial man who had been refreshing himself in the pantry, and not with punch, advanced to the center of the room, raising his hands.

"Ladies and gentlemen, may I propose a toast that is brief and to the point; a toast to a great lady: Rachel Henderson Thorpe, one hundred years a queen!"

"Why, thank you, Howard, thank you, everyone!"

The cup quivered in her hands, spilled a little punch into her lap. Addie, who had been dabbing away the tears which had sprung up obediently at Howard's toast, leaned forward to dab away the punch on her mother's skirt.

"Addie, don't *fuss* at me. A spot or two won't signify."

There was a little stir at the door as the gardener's three small boys were ushered in. All of them were clean, their hair still striped from a wet comb.

"Now, who are those?"

"Jepson's little boys, Mother."

"Whose?"

"*Jepson's*, Mother. They've come to see the cake. They've never seen a cake with a hundred candles on it."

"Well, light it for them, then, somebody. They must see it lighted!"

One by one, as the two maids dipped above them, the hundred candles brightened, brightening the faces of the children: their eyes looked large and still, their wet hair gleamed, light seemed to shine behind their foreheads. Above them hung the kindly pleated faces of Bridie and Agnes, where nothing gleamed except the frames of Bridie's glasses.

The youngest boy, whose head was at table level, looked up at the candle flames and began to sing. The other two joined in, raggedly, piping after him on different levels.

> "Happy birthday to you,
> Happy birthday to you,
> Happy birthday Mrs. Tho-orpe,
> Happy birthday to you."

"Why, thank you, children, thank you very much. Agnes shall give you each a nice big slice—Agnes, please see that they each get a nice, big—Addie, are you wiping your eyes *again*? Why, in mercy's name? Why, this time?"

"The little boys, Mother . . . they're so . . . I just can't help it."

Mrs. Thorpe turned to those nearest her.

"My daughter is a woman of many emotions; all of them minor," she said, and paused for a moment, having surprised herself, before summoning up a rusty disused laugh. It sounded rather like the croaking of a pheasant.

The others joined her, even Addie; but Deirdre, who loved her grandmother, stepped up to her and took her hand.

"Never mind her, Granny," she murmured. "She's a ruthless old brute and always was."

"Oh, no, dear, no, no! She isn't, or at least she wasn't. I'm the only one who remembers her when she was young, after all—"

"All minor," Mrs. Thorpe repeated. "You young people must print that in your paper. You must be sure to print it." Her laugh turned into a cough, possessed her, shook her, and Addie sent Bridie for a pill and a glass of water.

"I'm the only one who can remember her when she was young," Addie continued, when her mother had subsided. "She was perfectly beautiful, you know. You've seen her pictures; they don't do her justice. Those old photographs—the people in them always look as if they'd been paralyzed while listening to a sermon. She was beautiful, Deirdre; and gentle and kind. Playful, too, at least until that dreadful summer when my brother and sisters . . . " She paused.

"Died," supplied Deirdre, who scorned euphemisms and the avoided word.

"Died. And sometimes even after that. If I could only make you see . . ."

But watching Deirdre watch her great-grandmother Addie knew that she could never make the child see or believe in that other woman who had once lived in the world, lived in this very house; that young blonde tender woman. . . . Thinking this, a certain memory returned to her as it often did: herself, a small child running and crying through a field of weeds; weeds all taller than she was, wet and harsh in the summer morning; and behind her—material for many a nightmare in her life—the pounding horror; the creature buckling and snorting, big as a locomotive, bigger and worse, because alive! How far and tall her mother had seemed running toward her in her long pink dress, her pink hands outstretched and terror in her face; briars ripped at her skirt and her hat fell off. They had seemed to run toward one another forever (and in memory would run forever) in the moment before they met and her mother seized her, lifted her in her arms and turned, stumbling, half-moaning, to run again.

And there at the fence her father was, by magic, to grasp them, lift them both, both at once, right over the rail, and just in time!

"Oh, Lawrence," her mother had cried, and burst into tears; and her father had held them tight in his arms, circled round and safe, while the huge boar, a Poland-China, rumbled and uttered gross snuffles of frustration at the fence rail.

"Dearest girl, it's all right now, it's all right. What a child you are, but what a brave child!" her father had said, pinning back a lock of her mother's blond hair. His fingers had been shaking, though, and she had seen them.

And now the blond hair was white and parched, the pink hand was like a withered root, and Mrs. Thorpe for years had been as tearless as a stone. And I wish I were the same thought poor Addie, whose tears flowed freely at so many things: music, the sight of children asleep, even perfectly worthless sentimental things that she despised: the appropriate appearance of the U.S. troops on TV, newspaper accounts of faithful dogs, the tinny voices of child actors. This treasonous response to the mawkish or obvious was a great trial to her, and instead of lessening seemed to be increasing with age.

The gardener's boys were led away with frosting stuck to the corners of their mouths. Two were persuaded to push a hand for an instant into the dry grip and clutch of Mrs. Thorpe's; but the youngest boy refused, pulling back, appalled.

The photographers put away their cameras, the reporters their notebooks; they took their leave and departed. Mrs. Thorpe was worn out now and looked it, and this caused among the remaining gathering of relatives and friends a sort of reviving rustle; the stir of an unadmitted conspiracy. Soon they could get the whisky out; soon they could smoke. . . .

"Addie, I would like another cup of punch."

"Oh, Mother, I don't think I would if I were you."

"Addie, I *want* more."

"Mother, you know it gives you gas!"

Addie suddenly spoke sharply. Sometimes, not often, but this was one of the times, she felt that she had been robbed by her mother of her own old age: that she was denied the peace, consideration, personal crotchets and self-pampering that her years demanded, and instead must forfeit these to serve another, remaining, herself, a sort of septuagenarian adolescent, a permanent handmaiden. And why was this?

But she knew why.

Addie had married rather late; just under thirty. She was not beautiful, or flirtatious, or assertive; and had been slowly accustoming herself to the idea that she might never marry. And then all at once, in a matter of weeks, she had fallen in love, was loved in return; was married. Her husband had come from a distant state, different in every way from her own, and it was there that they had gone to live and lived until his death. The marriage had lasted nearly thirty years, and during the course of it they had reared their children, made their friends, had the heart of their life's experience. She had been busy from morning till night, gregarious, capable, a certain power in the community. She knew all this, thought of it often, tried to revive emotion in recollection, but tried in vain. *What* she had been during those years she could not imagine; at least it was impossible for her to regain in memory, even for an instant, the attitudes and feelings that had been hers so strongly during that life.

Because after it was over, back in her mother's house, she had returned to what she had been before; to what she had been during childhood and youth: the one who was left; the only one who had not died, and who must make amends for-ever. Even now, though she knew better, was white-haired, a grandmother, this was what she had come home to be, ridicu-lous though it was. . . .

Mrs. Thorpe, luckily, had forgotten about the punch. Her wishes were often becalmed in this way. Still, she knew she wanted *something*. A small gnarled sound came from her stomach. Ah, that was it!

"Addie, I'm hungry. I want to go up to my room and have my supper."

"Yes, Mother."

Howard and Helen helped Mrs. Thorpe to her feet and supported her from the room. Addie followed. The balsam pillow in the high-backed chair revealed a message stamped on it in green letters: "I Pine for Thee and even Balsam." But it was the only pillow that suited the old woman's back.

It was already dark at half past eight. Deirdre and her young man drifted out of doors. Behind them in the living room the older people sat resting from all the food and drink, relaxed and garrulous.

Upstairs, Addie, with Agnes attending, was preparing her mother for the night. Carefully, carefully, respectful of all joints and muscles, Mrs. Thorpe was eased into her bed. (Board under the mattress, four pillows at the head, heating pad turned to medium between the sheets, a folded afghan for the shoulders, and on the table under the light that burned all night, a radio, one sleeping pill, a bottle of cough medicine and spoon, Kleenex, spectacles, a reading glass, a detective story begun over and over again, the Bible that was never opened: all part of a machine for riding out the night.)

"A hundred years old," said Mrs. Thorpe, yawning cau-tiously. "I've lived a century. I don't believe it. And I don't want it. I *do not want it!*"

"Mother, how can you talk like that," Addie said. "Why, I think it's just wonderful."

Wonderful. What's wonderful about it, Mrs. Thorpe thought, watching Addie, an old woman herself, moving about the room. That old woman who looks after me. My daughter. My daughter? . . . Somewhere out of the great fading volume of memory she saw her little girl come screaming toward her through the weeds; baby teeth showing, tears scattering . . . And behind her the beast, the pounding beast! . . . Oh, that warm, frantic bundle snatched up to her frantic heart! . . . How she had run for her life, gasping and stumbling, and there, sent by Providence, was Lawrence to lift them both, both at once he was so strong—right over the fence! She remembered how close he had held them, he and she with the child between them, all of them trembling and two of them crying.

Yes, she had loved that little girl. But the child had been smothered by womanhood, buried by age. She was just as dead now as all the others. Dead years and years ago . . .

"What was it I said, Addie, that made them laugh? 'My daughter is a woman of many feelings—' "

" 'Of many emotions,' Mother. 'All of them minor.' "

"That's it, that's it." The rusty laugh croaked forth again. Mrs. Thorpe levered herself cautiously back against the high pillows, her agate eyes turned toward the ceiling.

"All of them trivial, was it?"

"All of them minor, Mother."

"That's it, 'all of them minor.' Not bad for a—for a—now what do they call those people? I know! Not bad for a centenarian."

"Shall I open the window a little, Mrs. Thorpe?" Agnes asked.

"Well, I don't know. What is the time of year?"

"Mother, it's September tenth. Your birthday! You *know* that!"

"Then open it, of course. Open it! I like to smell the clematis this time of year."

Agnes parted the long curtains at the window and lifted the sash. A night sound of crickets came into the room.

The light on the terrace disturbed Deirdre and her lover at their kissing.

"Don't move, darling. Wait. Maybe it will go out again."

"No, it won't. Great-granny's light stays on forever like the flame at the tomb of the Unknown Soldier. In a minute she'll start the radio, too. Let's go down by the pool."

"What smells so sweet?" he asked as they walked slowly and unevenly, with their arms around each other, across the dark lawn.

"Clematis. Dusty. Like dust with perfume in it."

"It is. But who would ever think of that but you?"

After this they were silent, absorbed in their love-making. Now and then a leaf crept down the air.

From Mrs. Thorpe's window a man's loud voice spoke suddenly.

". . . be purchased at half the original price. Men, don't wait! Go *now* to Bridgeport's Bond Street Store and see—"

The voice was summarily stilled; replaced by a woman's, singing "Love for Sale"; silenced in turn and replaced by the opening measures of "Invitation to the Waltz," which was allowed to run its course.

"John. John, tell me something. Will we ever get old?"

There was no answer to Deirdre's question. None was needed. They both knew they would never grow old.

Morgan's Rest

The driveway, partly graveled, curved away amongst a great elderly stand of landscape evergreens: firs, cedars, Norway spruces. Only crows and other rasping birds rose up from the dark boughs.

"Morgan's Rest," read Francesca, stopping her bike. The name stood out in gravestone letters on one of the gateposts. There was a tinge of moss on the edges of the letters.

"Gorgon's Rest, I call it," said her cousin Benedict. "Gorgon's Roost would be still better. That's what lives in there, brother, a gorgon!"

"Who really, though?" said Francesca. They stood there in the failing light leaning on their bicycles, glad to stop from the long, slow uphill walk.

"A gorgon named Morgan, no kidding," her cousin insisted.

"Listen, I'm telling you, I saw her once. God! It was fall, last year, no, year before; we were out for the weekend. Dev Riley and I were hacking around, walking, not riding our bikes, I forget why. And we came to this driveway and decided to see what it led to. It goes down; it winds and goes downhill with a lot of dark trees around, sort of spooky (we were only ten then), and at the end there was an open space with a big house in the middle of it. It looked all shut up and abandoned. The blinds were closed, and there were vines all over, even over the blinds, and the hedges hadn't been clipped for years and some of the trees were dead. But in the cleared-away place beside the house there was a birdbath sitting on the statue of some kid. A little naked kid, and the queer thing was there were clotheslines all strung around, strung from the porch to a tree and another tree, or from the porch to the statue of the kid and from there to a shed in the bushes. Clotheslines everywhere and not for hanging clothes on, I don't think. It was like a big crazy spiderweb; we couldn't figure it out. We were pretty quiet at first, we were whispering, because it really was spooky. There was an orchard back of the house so we went to get some apples, but they weren't any good so we started throwing them at each other because they were pretty hard still. You know, just horsing around; and then Dev—I don't know why—but Dev started throwing apples at the house, and they sounded like bullets, so I did, too; then all of a sudden we heard a door slam, and a loud deep voice was calling: 'Stop that! Go away! You boys go away!' And there on the porch this old woman was standing. Tall. All dressed in black! But it was the look on her face— Oh, God, it was awful—she had these great big coal-black eyes, and her hair was hanging down, raggedy old witch's hair, and she looked like that gorgon, that main principal gorgon—you know, what's-her-name—"

"Medusa?"

"Yeah, Medusa, and I was so scared—I admit it—and so was Dev (we were only ten then) that we could just about taste it, and we beat it out of there and never went back again, either."

"Who was she, did you ever find out?"

"No. Never asked. We went back to the city next day and I almost forgot about it, till now; we never use this road. Well, come on, let's move, Fran. Fran*cesca!*"

"I wish you wouldn't call me that. Imagine naming anybody named O'Brien, Francesca!"

"I don't think they think about the kid when they name it. I think they're sort of showing off; being different or something. How'd you like to be named Benedict, for God's sake?"

"Everybody calls you Ben."

"*Benedict*. It sounds like some old loony medieval monk. Friar Benedict, little brother to the bats."

Francesca thought this was extremely funny and so did he, and they were laughing as they reached the top of the hill, coming up at last into late sunshine. The Alberly fields lay below them, a placid map divided by the rambling slow river. Far away, Benedict's house was hidden in its square of trees.

"Lucky! Living here all summer every summer," Francesca said.

"So what? You're here all summer yourself this year."

"I know. And you know why?"

"Why?"

"I think it's because my father's finding out if he wants to get married again. I think he wants me out of the way so he can see if he can make up his mind."

"No kidding. Is it someone special, or is he just looking around?"

"Somebody special, I think. Mrs. Bates, her name is. I don't know her very well, but I hate her."

"Why? What's she like?"

"Big. She's got a big front that sticks out. Two big fronts. I hate that. She's about thirty or forty but her hair is still brown, and she's rich. I guess. She smells of perfume and wears bracelets and has a Thunderbird."

"*That's* not bad."

"No, that's not bad, and I like her dog: a corgi named Trick. Her husband's dead."

"Any kids?"

"No, and that's another thing. Oh, I suppose she's not so terrible. It's just . . . she's always being so *sweet* to me and giving me presents and calling me 'honey'! I wish she wouldn't. I wish . . ."

But Francesca was sick to death of her wish. She leaped onto her bike. "Come on, you snail!" And down the hill they went, faster and faster, blinded by the low sun. Anything—any feeling—could be cured by speed, and if one fell off the bike it could be cured by pain.

Francesca's mother had died when she was a baby. There was a picture of her on Aunt Barbara's bureau. Sometimes when she was certain no one would see her Francesca tiptoed into the large married-looking bedroom and examined the picture: a young, serious face with large eyes and a beautiful mouth. There were other pictures at home: one in her room, as a matter of fact, but most of these were smiling and looked different, falser, as if her mother had been smiling with her breath held, the way one does in a photographer's studio.

Francesca would stare at the picture and try to make it remember something for her, but it never did. If she heard someone on the stairs, or a door closing, she would scurry silently from the room, and nobody knew that she had been there. One's mother is a very private thing if she is dead. In the same way, an almost superstitious way, it was impossible to ask voluntary questions; but if someone should speak to her of her mother, tell her things about her, Francesca listened intently and never forgot a word. In this way she had learned that her mother as a girl had been impetuous, absent-minded, and high-spirited; that she had been a befriender of animals, even of a skunk; that she had hated cucumbers (a trait that Francesca believed to be inherited, since she hated them herself); had loved dancing and skating and playing jokes; and had received nine proposals of marriage before she was twenty, including one from a man who later became famous by being jailed for embezzlement.

She was reckless, too.

"They dared her to climb Pinnacle Rock, and you know how steep and narrow *that* is," Aunt Barbara had said. "I begged her not to; 'you'll be killed,' I said; but she just kicked off her slippers and started climbing. I simply couldn't watch. And when she got to the very top and was perched there she looked down and kind of squealed. 'Oh, Barb, I'll never get down again,' she said; and it was about the only time I ever saw her scared. She *couldn't* get down, either, she just *couldn't;* so in the end—what do you think—we had to call the Alberly Fire Department! They had to come with the hook and ladder and bring her down like a treed cat!"

Aunt Barbara said this laughing, and then abruptly her eyes and mouth turned serious, her whole face faded, and she sighed. It was partly because of that look and that sigh that Francesca did not ask questions about her mother. Everyone was the same: they would be telling a story of fun or mischief, smiling as they told it, and then all at once the light would go out and the sigh would come, ending every story sadly.

All that summer her father's letters continued to mention Mrs. Bates with a sort of gentle and increasing pressure. Mrs. Bates had won the ladies' singles tennis tournament at the club; she had bought a beautiful old house on the Cape; she had suffered from hay fever late in June; had taken up the study of Spanish in July. And in each letter before her father signed his own love to Francesca, he presented her with love that was sent by Mrs. Bates. Francesca scrupulously answered every letter, and never mentioned Mrs. Bates a single time.

But it was different on August eleventh, which was Francesca's birthday, because on that day, having consulted by letter with Aunt Barbara ("a point that redounds greatly to her credit," Aunt Barbara said, in private, to Uncle Owen), Mrs. Bates sent Francesca a birthday present of a corgi, just like Trick: bandy-legged, with four white spats, and eared like a gazelle. "Gee, I don't think this Mrs. Bates sounds so bad," Benedict said enviously, being between dogs himself.

But Francesca, won though she was, enchanted though she was, declared that the dog smelled of Mrs. Bates's perfume— "stuff called 'leur blur' "—and the first thing she did was to give him a bath.

"That's a sure way to kill a relationship with a dog," Benedict prophesied. But the corgi proved kindly and forgiving, and he seemed to know from the beginning whom he was meant to love.

"Anyhow you'll have to write to her now, because you'll have to thank her," Benedict said, not willing to see bliss unflawed.

"Oh, I *suppose* so."

Francesca wrote the letter dutifully, expressing gratitude, and explaining that the dog had been named Jones "because that was the most Welsh name my uncle could think of."

"I didn't put 'love' at the end of it, though," she told Benedict. "I put 'yours truly.' "

Jones was an all-but-perfect dog; old enough to be housebroken and young enough to be enthusiastic and original. He had an optimistic readiness for anything. Whenever she thought of that summer afterward, Francesca's mind would hear the clicking scurry of Jones's claws on the hall floor when she called him to go for a walk.

Each day, returning from swimming or tennis, she took him for a walk. Sometimes Benedict went with them. They rambled over stubbled fields, tore their way through rank late-summer woods, as Jones rooted and whimpered, getting his ears skeined with cobwebs, and beggar's-lice stuck to his coarse smooth coat.

The countryside was changing—drying out and toughening; yellow and brown came into the fields, black into the trees and hedges. The nights were still, and though not cold, one thought of coldness; one thought of the North. Francesca would not think about the winter. Perhaps if she did not think about it it would never come.

But the days grew fewer. They grew so few she had to count them. She walked faster and farther every afternoon, as if somehow she could walk away from the last day of all instead of only toward it.

And finally it was there: the last afternoon.

"Come, Jones," Francesca called, and immediately there was the scurry of clicking, the prancing spats, the barks and vertical leaps.

"It's the very last time," she told him mournfully.

That day they took a new direction—across Mr. Marble's cow pasture, over a bridge where a fat boy was fishing, across somebody else's pasture and up into somebody else's woods. It was a fine windless day. If Francesca and Jones had stood perfectly still they might have heard the dropping of an acorn; the sidle of a dry leaf down the air. But they were not still. Francesca scuffled leaves and kicked at twigs; Jones snorted and yelped as he hunted.

"Damn," Francesca said aloud. "Oh, damn, damn, damn!"

This word was not new to her, but it was rather new to her to say it, and gave her a certain biting satisfaction.

She had not seen these woods before, and maybe she was lost, but it didn't matter.

"Hell!" she said, slamming a stick against a tree trunk. "And damn and hell and damn!"

Then she began to sing. She sang "hell and damn" over and over and Jones barked, and everything was better.

After a while the trees thinned out. She was coming to something, and when she emerged from the woods she saw that it was an orchard, warped and perishing. There was a winy smell; wasps veered and reeled above the grass.

"What is this place?" Francesca asked of Jones.

Beyond the orchard stood a large steep-gabled house, hairy with vines. The shutters were all closed, knitted into place with vines, and some slats were missing. A deserted house. From the railing of a porch at one side an unusual number of clotheslines was spun out in rays.

Then Francesca saw the simpering marble child in the yard, and the backs of her knees turned cold and her scalp had a sudden wrinkled feeling.

"Jones! Jones! Come here!" She tried to yell in a whisper.

But Jones had caught sight of a cat sitting on the porch steps licking its shoulder, and he was off to war.

After him Francesca ran, stumbling over fallen apples, skidding on rotten ones. Her heart hurt and she was nearly crying.

"Jones! Oh, Jones!"

The cat waited till the last moment, then leaped to the porch railing, where it humped itself up and hissed.

The porch door banged open.

"You boys go away!"

The voice, strong and deep, could have been mistaken for a man's; but it belonged to a tall, old woman, with charred black eyes and hanging hair. The Gorgon.

"Boys, take your dogs and go away!" she repeated, looking

straight at Francesca; leaning forward over the railing, braced on her knuckles, staring.

"But—but I'm not a boy," Francesca's voice cheeped out in quavers. She held up one of her pigtails, foolishly, to prove it. "See?"

"No, I can't see," the old woman said. "I'm blind."

Francesca took a single step. Backward instead of forward.

"Blind?"

"Of course. That's why I thought you were a boy. All that hullaballoo. Boys do come here sometimes to throw things and break things."

"But they never would, I know they wouldn't," babbled Francesca. "If they knew that you were . . . that you were . . ."

"Blind," said the woman impatiently. "Why are people so afraid to say it? Blind, blind, blind. A perfectly straightforward word. Using it can't make me any blinder."

She leaned farther forward. With her dark staring eyes and her head trembling a little, she did look frightening. But not as frightening as Benedict had said; and not like a gorgon. Whoever heard of a gorgon without sight? The very thing about a gorgon is what she can do to you by looking at you . . . if you look back.

Jones was acting like a fool: yelping compulsively and performing his vertical leaps, though the cat had now attained the roof and sat there watching without concern, wafting its tail gently, as a woman, bored at the opera, might waft a fan.

Francesca turned on Jones, seized him and closed his muzzle with her hand. "You shut up," she said severely, and to the woman: "I'm sorry he's so noisy."

"He's not very large, is he? He doesn't sound large. Are you holding him?"

"Yes," Francesca said.

"Then would you bring him to me, please. . . . It's years since I've touched a dog."

Ashamed to hesitate, Francesca carried Jones up the porch steps to the old woman, whose hand reached out, blotted and veined; rattling with rings.

"How different from a cat! The fur so live and bristled . . . That cold wet nose . . . and what ears: a pair of sails . . . Oh, I miss a dog. I never was without one when I had my sight: but now I keep cats for company; they never let you step on them, and they do one thing a dog can't do; they purr."

Francesca was gratified by Jones, who was now being not only forbearing but flattering. He put out his tongue and paid the old lady the compliment of licking her hand.

She gave a sound of pleasure. "And I'd forgotten that. Cats' tongues are made of emery."

Francesca examined the porch: clean and bare. Nothing there but a wicker chair, a table, cats' dishes in the corner; and she saw that every clothesline, of the many tied to the railing, had a loose end hanging, and to each of these a different object was secured: a dangling amulet. She saw a key, a bottle-stopper, a sash weight, a pewter spoon, a curtain ring, the china torso of a doll.

She lifted the key, examined it, and let it drop. It rang as it swung back against the wood.

"You're looking at my clues?"

The old hand gave Jones a final pat, dismissed him, and reached out to find and hold the doll.

"I touch this and I know the cord attached to it will lead me to the orchard. The spoon takes me to the cellar, the key to the drying yard, the stopper to the woodshed. And so on."

"What a good idea," Francesca said politely. "Do you have them in your house, too, Mrs. Morgan?"

"Miss. No, I don't need them there. I know the house the way I know the table nine. I memorized it the way I did the table nine. When I knew I was going to be blind I walked all over it with my eyes shut: upstairs, downstairs, attic, cellar, over and over again. Locks, doorknobs, windows that stuck; I studied them. I studied them all until I knew them better than by heart. And then I closed off all the house except the little part I live in. But still I know it, every bit! . . . Outdoors is harder to learn, though: the bushes sound different with leaves on them, and they stand closer; the wind can blow away your sense of place—and then sometimes there's snow. Outdoors is different all the time; so Harvey Larkin spun me my lines. He comes each week to mow the grass and see if I'm alive or dead."

Miss Morgan reached for the handle of the screen door.

"Would you like to come in?"

Still holding Jones, Francesca followed her inside. Dusky in there; a faint smell of cat and age, but everything in order.

"Why, it's so neat!" she exclaimed, and then felt embarrassed to have shown surprise.

"Of course it's neat," said Miss Morgan with some spirit. "Things must stay in their places here, or I can never find them. And then one's so much neater when one cannot read. No books lying about, no newspapers waiting to be caught up with. No letters to or from anybody. The written word is responsible for a lot of mess. Come and have some tea."

Since this did not sound like an invitation, Francesca did not know how to refuse and, first dumping Jones out onto the porch, she followed Miss Morgan into the kitchen.

There, one would not have guessed that she was blind. She stepped about with perfect assurance, opening cupboard doors, jiggling the kettle to see if it was full. On a table by the window she put cups and saucers, a sugar bowl, some spoons. The kitchen was worn and clean, and it was light, the outside shutters being folded back or blown away. The polished wood stove breathed as though it were alive.

"Wouldn't a gas stove be easier?" Francesca asked.

"Easier, but not so good to listen to," Miss Morgan said. "Snorts and pops, that's all you get from gas stoves."

"What is your name?" she asked abruptly.

Francesca admitted her detested name.

"Where do you live?"

Francesca explained that she was visiting, and where and with whom.

Miss Morgan's eyes widened and were turned on Francesca: one would have sworn they saw her.

"Then you must be . . . you *must* be Belinda Barlow's daughter!"

"Yes, I am. I was . . . I mean she's—"

"Dead, yes, I know," Miss Morgan said, using the word just as she had used the word "blind," stripping the dread from it, robbing it of any superstitious fealty. "Such a pretty girl she was, and lively!"

"You *knew* her?"

"I was her piano teacher for a year. (That's what I did when our money was lost: taught music.) Your mother came to Alberly for a year—health? trouble at school?—I don't remember; but she was staying with her aunt, your *great*-aunt, where you are living now. She had a talent for music, but not the interest. She had talents in all directions, and a real gift for trouble. A wonderful girl. Cream? Sugar?"

"Both, please. What did she look like?"

"Stormy, lovely; wild dark hair, blue eyes. Nice teeth. The boys had just begun to notice her and she knew it. She was thirteen, or perhaps fourteen."

"Oh, tell me about her, please," begged Francesca, begging, outright, for the first time. Was it because Miss Morgan couldn't see her face? Or because of the way she was able to say the word "dead"?

"One thing she had was a nice voice, a caressing voice,

really. When you're blind you know a lot about people by their voices; even their remembered voices. . . . A cookie?"

Miss Morgan held out a cardboard box and Francesca plucked a stony disk from it.

"Stale," the old woman said carelessly, as she bit into one. "I must have had them since Thanksgiving. Yes, she had a soft, well-modulated voice—even a dignified voice. It quite belied her recklessness and mischief. Because she was a handful in her way. Yes, these are very stale. . . ."

"In what way?" insisted Francesca.

"Well, for example, there was a boy—a poor, fattish boy— what was his name? Harold something. He'd begun to notice her all right, but she couldn't abide him, so one night, and just for devilment, she called him up and told him she was locked in the public library—the librarian had overlooked her—and asked him to come and rescue her; so he jounced and panted down to the library, banged on the door and shouted; finally broke a window to get in, and, of course, she wasn't there. All Harold—Harold *Belcher*, that was his name—how could I forget it? All Harold Belcher got was arrested. Oakley White-head arrested him for breaking and entering, and disturbing the peace."

"My goodness," Francesca said.

"Well, Belinda came to his rescue right away, of course. She had a heart, a warm heart, though it wasn't always on duty. And such is the way of humankind that in spite of all the trouble she'd caused him, and the way he was laughed at, Harold Belcher doted on her more than ever!"

"What else did she do?" said Francesca greedily. She bit into her cookie. Miss Morgan was right. It was hard as a rock and tasted of cardboard.

"Well, one thing I remember very well indeed. Every spring in my teaching days, my pupils gave a recital. It was given in the old Trustworthy Homeowners' Auditorium on Flood

Street. Bunches of lilacs, so it must have been May. (I never smell lilacs without hearing the 'Volga Boat Song.') Everybody dressed up; relatives of all ages; a printed program.

"It was a fine sunny afternoon, and everybody rustled and crackled and coughed and then they were quiet. Little Karen Billmeier was first. 'Für Elise.' She played it all through without a mistake, and it sounded just as stale as this stale cookie. Everybody clapped. Then Baby McCauley—he was called Baby because he was so enormous—*he* had the 'Volga Boat Song' that year, and he got stuck in the middle of it and everybody suffered, and he started over again and got stuck again, and started over again and holding his breath—we all held our breath—he sweated himself over the obstacle and got to the end. Everyone clapped with relief.

"Then it was your mother's turn. Her number was 'Rustle of Spring,' by Christian Sinding—a difficult thing, but she knew how to play it well and wasn't self-conscious. I was sure I could relax. She was wearing a yellow dress and looked perfectly lovely—a perfect young girl; and she went to the piano and sat down so prettily, so daintily, smiled shyly out at the audience, then bent over and began pounding out something called 'Cow-Cow Boogie'!"

"My goodness!" Francesca said again.

"Yes indeed, my goodness is right. But I let her play it to the end. She felt guilty, I knew. Her cheeks were red and she kept giving me little sideways looks. When she was finished there was a sort of uproar—indignation, but some of the fathers were laughing, I noticed. I stood up and said: 'We were to have heard the "Rustle of Spring"; Miss Barlow chose this substitute of her own accord, and now, Miss Barlow, you are dismissed from the Trustworthy Homeowners' Auditorium as of this moment, and from my classes forevermore!' More tea?''

"No," Francesca said. "Thank you. But what happened then?"

"Well, she and her aunt and uncle all skulked out and I knew she'd get a dressing-down at home, but she deserved it. The concert continued in a subdued way; I hardly heard it.

"And then next day, a rainy day, your mother, Belinda, came to my house. Crestfallen, she looked. I let her in. 'Miss Morgan, will you forgive me?' she said, and I said, 'No.' Then she said: 'I only did it to get four dollars,' and she explained that she wanted to get a birthday present for her best friend and didn't have a penny, so some of her wicked companions had offered her the money as a bribe, on one of two conditions: it was either 'Cow-Cow Boogie' at the recital, or kissing Harold Belcher before witnesses; 'and you know I *couldn't* have done that,' she said, appalled at the idea.

"I was very stern, and told her that she had simply compounded the felony by accepting a bribe. She was really downcast; then she said: 'Miss Morgan, could I play my piece for you the way I should have yesterday?' and I said, 'No.' But she went to the piano anyway and sat down and played 'Rustle of Spring.' Well, it's an old-fashioned, sentimental thing, full of grandiose arpeggios, but she played it very well. Nothing stale about *her;* and I watched her in the rainy light, so lovely and young and contrite—contrition became her— and I thought, as I often have, how many people a person is! A human being is more many-sided than a prism; he has sides he shows the world, sides he only shows to special others, sides he doesn't know he shows to others, sides he doesn't even guess he has. No, nobody is simple, no matter how he'd like to be. So, watching her, and thinking these things, and plagued by my own troubles (I had many, and was beginning to be concerned about my sight), I felt tears in my eyes, but I never let *her* see that! No, indeed!

"When she stopped I said: 'You played that quite nicely, Belinda, and I'm going to forgive you. But heaven knows what the future has in store for you: I expect you'll elope with a jewel-thief—'"

"She *was* proposed to by an embezzler," Francesca said excitedly, then on a more sober note: "but she didn't marry him."

"No? I'm surprised." Miss Morgan laughed again, remembering. There was no regretful fading to her amusement. There was no sigh. For once the story had not ended sadly.

"Do you look like your mother?" she asked unexpectedly.

"No," Francesca said. "Old plain brown hair, braided. Old plain brown eyes. Just ordinary."

"But you have her voice," Miss Morgan said. "You have her voice exactly."

Francesca, remembering the words "soft," "caressing," "dignified," blushed at the sudden knowledge of possessing a valuable thing she had not guessed she had.

Miss Morgan abruptly put her hand to her head.

"Good heavens, my hair!" she cried, and rising quickly, almost as quickly as a girl, she went to the window sill where there was a jar of hairpins. Her fingers were deft and knowing; she had no mirror and would never need one in her life. The hair was smoothed, tamed into a knot at the nape. It made her look a different person. (How many people a person is! Francesca thought.)

"You must have believed I was a witch. At least, thank heaven, *I'm* relieved of my appearance! But I get careless, seeing no one, or almost no one. Most people think I'm dead, I imagine, and I don't miss them. I play my piano and listen to the radio and talk to my cats and through my cats to myself. The things I say often surprise me. You know, as long as you can still surprise yourself—even if unpleasantly—life isn't dull.

I'm never lonely. . . . But it would be nice if you would come to see me sometimes. . . ."

"Next summer when I'm here, I'd like to," said Francesca, surprised because this was the truth.

She and Jones went home by way of the road, walking up-hill in the shade. She was anxious to tell Benedict about Miss Morgan; she felt unreasonably indignant with him, as though she herself had somehow been misjudged.

The woods by the road were still and brooding. She was glad when they reached the top of the hill. There lay the map of fields, just as it had two months ago, but gilded now by the late season and the late sun that stared her in the face.

Jones went bounding down the road, but Francesca walked slowly. She felt happy; and suddenly, for no reason at all that she could see, she thought of Mrs. Bates and found that she was thinking of her in a new way; wondering about her.

Free Dust

"He always has; it's his way," Mary Raynor said to her house guest, Zaida Burton. "I suppose he always will."

"Who will always what?" asked her son, Timmy, coming into the room with a plate in his hand. Something about himself, probably, he thought.

"None of them have manners nowadays," said Mary, explaining Timmy to Zaida. "Manners are not supposed to be taught any more; they're supposed to develop gradually and naturally like their Adam's apples. Your father," she said, turning to Timmy. "I was telling her how your father always goes down and builds something when he's upset or angry. Builds and swears. Listen . . ."

They were silent. From the workshop in the basement came a sound of hammering accompanied by a masculine voice. No words were distinguishable.   .

148

"That way he's gotten a lot of repairs done," Timmy said.

He went upstairs to his room carrying the plate. He had just made himself five meat-loaf sandwiches because he was going to put Handel's Oratorio on his record player.

"And not only swearing," Mary said, when he was out of earshot. "The words he uses! You know those *words*. The kind you see in cement."

"Elmo? Oh, I can't believe it. Elmo!" cried Zaida, thinking of him.

Mary bristled slightly. "Just because he looks mild," she said. "I know that. He does look mild. But if you knew him as I do you'd be very much surprised. Elmo has character traits that no one suspects."

When she spoke of him Mary's conversation became a sort of Procrustean bed for Elmo. If you said he was meek, she implied that he was a tiger; if you said that he was a tiger (few would), she described his gentleness; if you praised his constancy, she hinted at lewdness. And it is possible that there was an element of truth in all these aspects, hinted and revealed, since Elmo was, of course, a human being.

"What's he teed off about now?" said Timmy, coming into the room again. He had forgotten the Pepsi-Cola.

"Dad? Oh, it's the fifteenth, for one thing. He got hold of Hartnett's bill before I could hide it till the right time. He forgot to check the oil in the car and burnt out the bearings. And he's trying to stop smoking again. Nothing catastrophic, Timmy; just an accumulation of wrong things."

Timmy went on to the kitchen, whistling against his teeth. God, these middle-aged people, he thought. They can't see the woods for the cruddy little trees. Bills and trying to save money and fixing the roof and stuff like that. I won't live that way. As he slammed the refrigerator door he felt a stab of happiness: here was the cold bottle in his hand, and upstairs the meat-loaf sandwiches and the glorious music were waiting. He was sixteen years old and could see the woods, the forest, whole. Who cared about the separate trees?

He did not listen as he went through the living room or he might have heard a disconcerting parallel to his opinions.

"The longer we live the more we fall into the clichés of the comic strip, people like us," Mary was saying. "A rise in the anxiety graph on the first and fifteenth of every month. Old arguments about old habits that will never change; and all those halfhearted efforts to stay the effects of age—"

"I know. Exercises done for a few mornings, then abandoned," said Zaida. "Diets started and then abandoned."

Mary sighed loudly. "I always thought there must be a cure for it somewhere."

"A cure for growing old?"

"No, for one's attitude toward it. Painless aging, like painless childbirth . . . But I was going to tell you about Elmo. You notice the television cabinet?"

"I've been admiring it; I never thought that article of furniture could be so handsome. And what a good idea to have a sliding panel to cover the screen; that piece of dull glass, staring, can have such an effect on a room."

"That's what Elmo thought, too. Well, that cabinet has a history.

"There was one day last year when every single thing went wrong. It was November, right after the Big Storm (of course you didn't get it in Virginia, but you probably read about it; it was just as bad as any of the hurricanes), and here we were with no power, no water, no light, and we'd bought an electric stove, like fools, so of course we couldn't really cook. We just kept roasting hot dogs in the fireplace. I haven't been able to look at one since.

"Also it was Sunday, and you know how terrible that can be. And it was cold and gray. The *worst* day. Timmy had a bad cold and I had my sinus, and I kept telling myself this, too, will pass.

"Well, Elmo has a cousin (thank heaven it's his cousin, not mine) who lives in Michigan. His name is Norwood Creamer, and he's perfectly nice; I always thought he was perfectly nice, but he has this wife! Her name is Eula, Eula Creamer. She has very arched nostrils and splendid teeth; white and strong and plentiful. She's never had a filling in her life; she tells you that, and opens her mouth wide to give you the experience of viewing her molars. Simon-pure. She is extremely durable in every way. She's my age and hasn't one gray hair, and her skin is like a baby's, and her eyes are clear and lustrous. They protrude, but they are lustrous. When she talks she forms her words very distinctly as if she were speaking to someone a little deaf or very old; and she does something to the letter "r" —invigorates it—in a way I have never heard equaled. PRRResident EisenhoweRRR. ORRRganization. CRRReam-eRRR. And she's very well informed; knows all about legislative bodies and things like that. Remembers everything; can talk business on an equal footing with the men, and child-rearing on an equal or slightly higher footing with the women."

"Has she children?" Zaida asked.

"Two. Boy and girl, bursting with vitamins and very successful. Each one president of the Student Council, and so on.

"Well, as I was saying, here we were on this dreadful day with all our crippled appliances—when who should blow in at exactly the worst time, about two in the afternoon, but the Creamers! Elmo was just getting well into his Sunday nap, under a litter of newspapers, and I'd settled down with the double-crostic when I heard a car door slam outside and then voices. Or, rather, That Voice; and I knew right away who it was, and my heart sank. I had thought them a thousand miles away, in Michigan.

"There was nothing to be done. We couldn't hide; the car was right there in the drive. And the door wasn't locked; Eula just gave one knock and flung it open. She doesn't stand on ceremony ever.

"I went to meet her and she was shouting 'Surprise! Surprise!' flashing and scintillating in a big overpowering way like the lighthouse at Narragansett Pier. She clasped me in a firm, sensible embrace and explained that they were on their way to see Connie—that's the daughter at college—and had decided to stop and see us.

" 'I said to Norwood, "Why Mary and Elmo are right on our way, Norwood, let's give them a *surprise!*" ' she said.

"When we came into the living room Elmo, poor creature, was just struggling up out of his nap, newspapers all over, beer can on the floor. My heart was wrung for him, he looked so helpless and appalled. Eula gave him one of her embraces, and then holding onto him, leaned back and scrutinized him.

" 'Elmo, have you been *well?*' she asked him.

" 'Can't complain,' Elmo said. 'Why? I look sick or something?'

" 'No-o,' Eula said. 'Not sick exactly. But your color does seem a little high.'

" 'Beer and sleep,' Elmo said. 'That's all that is.'

" 'But have you had a check-up lately?' Eula asked him. 'After fifty, all of us should have bi-yearly check-ups, you know.'

" 'I'm only forty-eight,' Elmo said.

"Eula just laughed ringingly.

" 'He really is only forty-eight, Eula,' I told her. She is the limit. If you said you were ninety-one, she'd just laugh that laugh, implying that you were really ninety-two and trying to cover up.

"I thought I'd better change the subject and began rattling on about the storm and how terrible it had been. (All the time I was snatching up newspapers and emptying ash trays, trying, in a hurry, to correct the awful impression of dishevelment the room had presented when they came in. I saw *that* in Eula's lighthouse glance.)

"And she would not permit me to have my storm. She came right back at me and described a cyclone she had experienced the year before in Kansas when her father's front porch had been ripped clean off the house and tossed away, and the Presbyterian steeple had blown into the next county. 'Nobody was killed,' she admitted grudgingly. Then she brightened up and said: 'But *many* were injured!'

"And it was she, of course, who caught the mantle of Florence Nightingale and set up a first-aid station in the public library. I'm sure everything she said was true. I'm sure she was a godsend to the community. But somehow, as she talked, she managed to make me feel that I had been timid and ineffectual in the face of Nature's violence, and that Nature's violence in the East was rather a joke anyway.

"So the afternoon went on like that; bad to worse. At five o'clock it began to rain and the fire started smoking. By that time Eula had criticized us for having the cat spayed, suggested a new color scheme for the dining room, recommended a superior brand of dishwasher to the one we'd just bought, and asked me tactfully why I didn't stop dyeing my hair.

" 'Mary,' she said. 'The good Lord knew what He was doing when He let women's hair go gray in middle age; it's so much more softening to the featuRRRes.'

"I could feel the wrinkles forming on my face, I tell you. And every now and then she would scrutinize Elmo with a worried little frown, and I began to think perhaps he *didn't* look so well.

"Timmy came in about six. He was fifteen then, so he was writing poetry all the time and we could *not* get him to the barber. He looked like Group Captain Peter Townsend. He was above talking to people, too; at least to adults. But Eula persevered. She pried an admission from him that he liked music, and collected records.

" 'Dave Brubeck, I'll bet, right, Timmy?' Eula said, knowingly. 'Jonah Jones? The Everly Brothers? The Beatles? Who *are* your favorites?' "

" 'William Boyce,' Timmy told her. 'Henry Purcell. Vivaldi.' "

"Eula looked dashed, for once.

" 'Contemporaneous with Bach,' Timmy explained. 'Music still uncorrupted by Romantic.'

"When he'd gone, Eula looked at me thoughtfully and said: 'Mary, have you ever thought of psychiatry for Timmy?'

"I said no I hadn't. At that moment I could have killed Timmy. I thought why couldn't he have had his hair cut and talked about Junior Gilliam, or something, just for once!

"Eula kept right on. 'Timmy's an only child,' she was telling me (news for me), 'and I have a theory that the only child *resents* the lack of sibling rivalry. He *resents* being deprived of a peRRRfectly natuRRRal outlet for his aggRRRessions.'

"I didn't dare look at Elmo, but I could feel him clear across the room beginning to heave and swell like milk coming to a boil.

"*Norwood* was just sitting there smoking his pipe, eyes half-closed, and I had the distinct impression that he'd turned Eula off; that he's able to turn off whatever she's saying, if he feels like it. Well, he'd *have* to. . . .

"But instead of doing anything drastic, Elmo just suggested a drink. He'd offered this before, but Eula had refused for both of them on the grounds that the sun was not yet over the yaRRdaRRRm. She doesn't really like to drink.

"So Elmo said, 'The sun is now *under* the yardarm. Way under. It is time.'

"Norwood said he thought so, too, and offered to help, but Elmo declined and went off to the pantry, where he was gone rather a long time, I thought. He came back with whisky for us and something odd-looking in the last of our old wedding-present cocktail glasses for Eula.

" 'I made it especially for you, Eula,' he told her with a little bow. 'It's called a Sunset Gun.'

" 'Goodness!' Eula said, but she took it and drank it right down like medicine. Then she looked surprised. 'Why, it's perfectly delicious, Elmo,' she said. 'Just as good as a soda. I believe I'd like another.'

"She grew very vivacious on the first one, and her eyes sparkled as she gave Elmo some helpful pointers on how to run his office; but after the second she suddenly fell silent and the eye-sparkle turned to more of a glaze. I had the dreadful thought that perhaps Elmo had poisoned her, and I could imagine how all our photographs would look on the front page of the *Daily News*. . . .

"And then Eula stood up, a little unsteady but decisive.

" 'Norwood, we must go,' she said. 'Or we'll never get a table at Howard Johnson's.'

" 'Why, listen, we can roast you a couple of franks right here, and we've got some nice canned kraut,' Elmo offered (oh, he can be wicked), and that really lent wings to their departure.

" 'Elmo, what did you put in Eula's drink?' I asked him, when they'd gone. 'Nitroglycerin, or something?'

"And Elmo said, 'Do you remember the bottle of Pernod that Roy Baskin brought us in 1939?'

"Well, I was shocked; we'd never even dared to taste the stuff ourselves. But Elmo said, 'Look here. The only way you can defeat Eula Creamer is by casting a doubt into her mind about herself, and that's next to impossible. The only time I ever saw it happen was after those Sazeracs at the Hardys'; so I just thought, well, maybe, a little of that *Pernod* . . . so I went and got it, poured in a jigger and a half, added some

Vermont maple syrup and a dash of vanilla and filled it up with cream and there you are.'

" 'What a terrible thing to do to *anyone!*' I said. But he didn't seem at all contrite; he'd gone over to the hall mirror and was looking at himself. He put out his tongue and looked at that.

" 'She's right,' he said, very depressed. 'I don't look well. My color isn't good.'

"Nothing I could say reassured him, and by and by he took a kerosene lamp and went down to the workshop. Pretty soon I'll hear him building something, I thought, and sure enough, in a few minutes I heard a sound of sawing and some muffled shouts. After a while he stopped shouting—he always does as the work starts to soothe him—and there was nothing but the sound of carpentry.

"He worked several hours that evening, and other evenings, and on weekends, too, but he wouldn't tell me what he was making. It was a surprise, he said. I thought, what on earth . . .

"Finally one evening he told me I could come down to the workshop. So I did, and what I saw was this long queer-looking box on the floor.

" 'What is it?' I asked him. 'Some sort of boat?'

"He just looked at me. 'Boat, hell,' he said. 'That's a coffin!'

" 'A *coffin!*' I said. 'Why? For whom?'

" 'For me,' Elmo said, and, Zaida, you never heard such satisfaction in a human tone. 'Look how I've mortised the corners,' he said, proud as could be. 'They might have grown together, the tenons fitted in like silk! Look at the finish, smooth as a pearl. Why, it's a work of art!'

" 'Elmo, I think that's *morbid!*' I told him. I didn't know whether to laugh or cry.

"But he was all enthusiasm. 'Fine wood!' he kept saying, slapping the coffin. 'Fine piece of redwood. Always knew I'd find a use for it.'

" 'Well, I think it's *morbid*,' I told him again, and he said not at all, that it was practical, economical, and forward-looking. So I thought, well, if it makes him happy—and I pretended to admire the horrible thing. (It really was very well made.)

"As I came up the basement steps I heard him whistling 'Scheherazade,' and that always means he's in a good mood. Oh, I tell you, Zaida, Elmo has character traits that nobody suspects!"

"I'm beginning to believe you," said her friend. "Is it still here, the coffin?"

"Wait. So the next day was Saturday. Elmo was out all afternoon, playing golf, *I* thought, but that night when we were going to bed he said, 'Mary, I went to see Everett Tucker today. I thought now I've got this coffin and all I might as well see about a place to put it, so I decided to pick out a plot.'

" 'Oh, Elmo, that's *morbid!*' I said (that's all I seemed to say to him those days). And Elmo said, 'So I went to the cemetery and walked around with Everett, and I don't know, it's the wrong time of year to pick out a plot. The grass was dead, the trees looked dead, the sky was gray, and nothing was making a noise except some crows, and they didn't sound cheerful. And—I don't know—all those mounds; those rows and rows of mounds, neat and identical as army cots . . . The whole place put me in mind of a big, tidy, gloomy dormitory . . . everything kept in line, you know, kept in line forever. . . .

" 'Everett showed me a plot he considered ideal; secluded, with a good view of the Fair grounds and choice company each side: the Listers, the Wendell Baileys, and so on. . . . And suddenly,' Elmo said, 'suddenly I couldn't stand any more and I said to him, 'Everett, listen; you've just lost a customer. Because I've changed my mind and I'm not going to die. I'm never going to die; but if through some slip-up I *do* die, I'm not going to be planted in this garden. No. I'm not going to be planted, period. I want my dust to blow in a lively place. I want free dust.'

"And then Elmo instructed me as to how he wished his ashes disposed of. Or 'dust,' as he prefers to call it. He said he wanted some scattered on the Fair grounds that that plot has such a good view of; and some on the portulaca bed at noon on a red-hot August day. He said to save a pinch to scatter in Shubert Alley sometime when I'd been to town to see a good show, and another for the Stadium during the Series. . . .

"I kept myself from saying this was morbid, because it seemed to be doing him a world of good. Even after we were in bed with the light out he kept holding up my sleep with new ideas: a little dust to toss into the woods on a September night when the katydids were racketing, for instance. And he suggested that it might be nice if I could sprinkle some over the brasses at the Philharmonic, 'but I doubt if it would be feasible,' he said, wistfully, and I said: 'I doubt it.'

"Then, as I was really drifting off, he jolted me back by saying: 'I know! A week or two before Christmas you could go to Macy's, when it's good and crowded, and from the escalator, just between the main and second floors . . .'"

"But that was too much. 'Elmo, you stop being MORBID!' I told him. 'Turn over, now, and go to sleep.'

"So he did, and slept like a baby, too.

"The next day was Sunday, a lovely day, and after breakfast I had the heart to ask him what he was going to do with the coffin. 'Sell it?' I asked him. 'Can you sell a thing like that? Would the Thrift Shop take it?'

"But Elmo said, 'No, sir. That's *good wood*, and it's not going to be wasted. I know just where to use it.' And the next thing I knew he was measuring the television set."

Zaida stared at the handsome cabinet across the room.

"For heaven's sake," she said.

"I know," said Mary.

From upstairs in Timmy's room came a throbbing of music; faint shrieks of song. Downstairs in the basement they heard the closing of a door, then footsteps running up the wooden stair; a sound of whistling.

"Listen," said Mary, holding up her hand and smiling. "It's 'Scheherazade.' So *that's* all right again."

A View by Lightning

To Maury, asleep in the armchair, a look of youth had been restored. Virginia, his wife, noticed it. Perhaps it was that the expression of pain, or the apprehension of pain, was gone from his face. Also he slept tidily, like a young person. His mouth stayed closed and he did not whinny or puff. His crutches stood propped against the wall, waiting.

The others were quiet for his sake; Jack, Maury's brother, was reading the paper gingerly, trying not to crackle, and Virginia was darning socks, a dull hypnotic task. Fay, her sister-in-law, had gone upstairs to do something to her face. Virginia gave a loud unexpected sigh and above the paper Jack's eyes looked at her sharply; he had very penetrating clear gray eyes. He smiled, and she smiled back. "So hot!" she whispered. But she loved the heat and did not know the reason for her sigh.

There had been a drought for weeks; the night air smelled of dust, and even the moths rustling and purring on the screens had a parched look. When the wind moved it made a papery restless sound, and far away the thunder mumbled to no purpose, as it had done for many nights.

Virginia looked again at her sleeping husband. He had the appearance now of what he really was; or at least of what he had been meant to be, she thought. People sometimes achieved this look, or perhaps returned to it, in sleep, or in the concentration of work, when they had forgotten themselves for a while. She remembered an elderly woman she had sat next to on a crowded bus one summer day. Furtively she had glanced again and again at the stern remarkable profile until the woman, sensing her attention, had turned and smiled. There was a jovial gleam of gold: "Brother, am I sweatin'!" she had said, and all the fantasies of heroic discipline, of tragedy and renunciation which such a face engendered, were dried up in the north light of reality. Yet probably she had her tragedies. . . . What would people be like if they were denied the power of speech, Virginia often thought. Without language and the habits of language and the influence that words impose on action, what would they be like? Without the cliché that demeans experience, or the exposure by language that alerts the snob, would men be wiser? Kinder? More what they ought to have become when they decided against being animals?

The thunder rumbled, this time a little louder; the pendants on the candelabra tinkled weakly. Fay's descending heels pecked at the hollow stairs, clack, clack, and she came into the room talking: "While I was upstairs I . . ." Then she saw Maury, stopped with an exaggerated look of caution and apology, and tiptoed humorously, in the manner of a small child, to the couch. "While I was upstairs I started packing," she whispered. "I thought I'd get the worst of it over with."

"Oh, I wish you and Jack didn't have to go!" Virginia said,

meaning it, thinking of the evenings ahead. Two years of pain and disappointment had made Maury testy, unreasonable, in many ways a stranger when they were alone.

"I wish we didn't! This has been such a *fun* time," said Fay, who had been badly affected by her name. She was small, thin, bright, and talked in a light rapid voice; her girlhood prettiness still cast a ghostly light in middle age. Having no children she had seemed to feel the need of being her own child; of being Jack's own child, affectionate, easily hurt, easily pleased—addicted to the use of the word "fun" as an adjective, and to the use of easy endearments which had not much to do with love.

"Oh, Virginia, you're darning *socks!*" she whispered reproachfully. "Jack, sweetie, look, she's darning Maury's *socks!* Don't you wish you had a wife like that? Honestly, I'm as helpless with a darning needle as I would be with a—with a cricket bat!"

"I still follow the custom I established when I was fourteen," Jack said. "When my socks get holes in them I throw them in the incinerator. You're a rare woman, Virginia."

"I'm not all that virtuous, never fear," she said. "I just wait and wait—sometimes I've waited a year—while the holey socks reproduce and multiply; then suddenly something falls in place, a shutter clicks, and a voice says: 'All right, go ahead. Darn.' And I do. I answer letters the same way." She held the sock up on her hand, smoothing the woven spot. "I don't recommend it as a method."

"Wool socks. An August night! Your shutter picked a queer time to click, sweetie." Fay put up her dry little hand to smooth her hair back. "Oh, it's so hot!"

Maury stirred, moved his head. In his sleep he was slowly preparing to wake up. Fay brightened.

"Shall we have a game later?"

"Of course, if you'd like."

Fay regained the look of what *she* really was whenever she played bridge, Virginia thought. Something calculating, mature, and shrewd came into her face and her manner. Even her voice deepened, her laughter took on a brusqueness, and she who was normally neat as a bird scattered her cigarette ashes and kicked her shoes off under the table.

The night had become breathless. Jack laid his newspaper aside. "Do you suppose the world's stopped turning?"

They all looked toward the windows. When had there ever been such stillness? The moths on the screens were motionless, transfixed; the wind was dead. Somewhere "Halt!" had been commanded. . . .

And then in their faces there was a great insult of light, and the air burst with a bang. Fay screamed, and Maury jerked from the last of his sleep, stared at them blinking. "What happened?"

"Lightning hit somewhere near," Jack said. "But the drought's over. Listen."

The thunderclap might have been a door or a floor exploding open. Rain now fell on the roof, on the land, in a vast heavy body like a dropped ocean.

"Oh God, the windows!" Virginia sprang up, shedding socks. "Help me, Fay!"

"Oh, sweetie, Jack will; I couldn't, I'm *petrified!* Maury, let me sit on the floor beside you."

"Come close, kitten—that's right. Put your head on my knee," Maury said, gentle from his sleep. He laid his hand on Fay's head, stroking the graying permanent curls as if she really was the child she played at being.

"Don't forget the attic," he called to the two running up the stairs.

The abrupt, comforting sound of windows closing came

from above, where the wet east wind was lashing at curtains, scattering letters, slamming doors. With each lightning flash the mirrors brightened all together.

"Remember the attic!" shouted Maury faintly, from below, and they went, more cautiously, up the last dark stairs.

The attic still held all of summer's heat, though rain was drubbing the roof and a draft turned the clothesbags slowly on their hooks.

"I can't budge this one," said Virginia, at the window, and Jack came to help her, knocking against luggage.

When they had mastered it together they stood for a moment, looking out. The lightning showed the willows blanched, bent double, the seething hedge, and the white, cowed river. Inside, it showed each to the other; each pale, startled face. He took her hand, then put his arms around her.

"No."

"Yes."

"Yes," she said. "Oh yes, oh yes . . ." How long have I known this without knowing it, she thought, and as if he had listened to her mind he said: "I've known this for a long, long time."

The thunder overhead was like the breaking of a city, and rain drove at the panes in gusts. Each time the lightning glared a dressmaker's form stood forth, firm and commanding; respectable as a queen. It had belonged to Maury's mother.

"Darling Virginia, I've loved you for years."

"And I've loved you for years. But I've only known it for a minute."

The lights started up and vanished, started up and vanished. The storm was like a cave around them and they were alone in it, private, wanting nothing but to know each other deeply and entirely, or, rather, they were like people who *have* known each other in this way, coming together again after a long separation, with recognition and relief and joy.

"But there's nothing we can do!" Virginia whispered.

"I know. Just this little minute and then nothing."

"To be this happy all at once and then to know that you'll be wretched. That's what's so awful: to know that one is going to be so hopelessly and tediously wretched!"

"I shouldn't have told you; I was never going to. The lightning jarred it out of me."

"Oh, thank God it did! I don't *care* about the wretchedness. . . ."

The sounds of enormous breakage continued overhead; and the queenly form continued to light up at intervals like a celebration of virtue.

"Vir-*ginia!* Ja-ack! Where are you? Come on down!" Fay's distant calling sounded peevish. She was ready for her game.

"We're just coming," Virginia answered in a brisk false voice.

"Oh, Jack, good-bye!"

"No. Never say it."

In the hall below she turned to look at him, and he took her hand and pressed the palm against his cheek.

As they came down the stairs into the living room they saw that Fay was still sitting on the rug by Maury's chair. She looked up at them.

"I would have brought the card table out but I was too terrified to open the—why, what's the matter? Why, Maury, see, I'm not the only coward in this family! Don't they both look scared? Maury, *look* at them. Don't they both look scared to death?"

Siesta

The sea had a noon sound. A smooth, heavy, breathing sound; a laziness, a measured weight, a deliberate fine rhythm all along the shore. Simply by listening to it you knew that the day was hot, and the sun just past its zenith. The cracked old green shade flapped into the room a little and was sucked back against the screen, but in its lurching forward it showed a glimpse of the day: the light-bleached sky, lawns, and beyond them the burning edge of beach; and still beyond that the strong blue of the sea. The starling fledglings in the nest in the vine made wild mewing sounds as food was brought them, but other birds were, for the moment, still.

Stephen lay on the bed with his eyes toward the window, watching the slipping glimpse of brightness, and then the sucked-back darkness, and then the glimpse again. In one hand he held a sticky candy wrapper and in the other a broken cap pistol; across his bony chest lay a garland of pear-conch eggs. From time to time he lifted one leg straight up in the air and then let it drop again, with a heavy thud, onto the bed. His legs were thin and his shins were scraped and bruised with scratched mosquito bites. His face was so covered with freckles that one seemed to be looking at him through a veil; there was chocolate all around his mouth, and his curly hair was stiff with salt. He was seven years old.

This was too old to be taking naps, he thought, but he understood that these were insisted upon because people needed a rest from him sometimes, and he didn't care anyway; he almost liked to lie here listening to the good sound of the sea. In his summer room, much bigger than his winter room back in the city, there were many things that he owned and valued: the summer things, the sea and country things like quarter-deck shells, and cracked disks of cork, and a piece of a seine, and the collections of bottle tops and sand dollars, the smooth washed stones and pieces of glass, the dead tan beetle, and the shattered halves of robins' eggs, and the gold-finch feather and the gull's feather, and the fish vertebrae which were shaped like spools, and the dried, speckled crabs and the big horseshoe crab that still smelled, and the dogfish eggs that some people call devil's pocketbooks.

The room had its own peculiar odor, and he was used to it and liked it; it smelled of the sea relics and dry rot, and very faintly of urine, because at night when he was sleepy he sometimes missed his aim at the chamber pot and struck the rug instead. His pillow smelled of damp feathers, and the paper in his hand smelled of chocolate, and when the shade breathed into the room there was a hot aromatic snatch of honeysuckle and bayberry and salt and melting asphalt. His nose, short, freckled, peeled, was an organ constantly in use, primitive in its alertness like that of an animal.

In the next room he could hear Sarah, his old nurse, stepping about softly, opening and closing drawers. But he was safe from her now; safe from her elderly sniping and commanding; her bony clutch which was half shove, half caress, and the long repetitious contentious flow of her conversation.

His father and mother, he knew, were where he had left them, stretched out in their chairs in the garden with the littered lunch tray between them, and he was safe from them, too; from his mother's pleading eyes in which there could be detected a certain desire for forgiveness; and safe alike from his father's massive, kind indifference and his infrequent towering displeasure.

He was free, for a while, from all the different kinds of loving that were demanded of him.

From far away in the core of the house came a distant clatter and murmur as the cook and her weekend helper washed the dishes and conversed. The house was everywhere alive; it hummed about him, but he was isolated within it like an infant bee in its cell. He, who because of his age and connections was in every way dependent, was free for a while to exercise an extravagant independence of his own invention.

Pretend they were all dead, he thought. All dead, and only children were left. And not all children, either. Just me and Jamie Nevins and Henry Mayer and Olive and Linda and Peter and Spike and the kids at school. We'd have the whole world to ourselves. We'd drive the cars and run the boats and stay up all night. But what about night, dark huge night with no grownups to yell for if you were afraid? But if there were no grownups there'd be nothing to be afraid of, he thought. We'd strike the matches and light the fires; we'd have real guns. We'd have all the guns. We'd let the animals out of the cages, and none of them would hurt us; not the tigers or lions, even, because they would be thankful to us for letting them out. Maybe some of the people wouldn't be dead; the bad ones would be still alive so we could punish them, and we would put them in the cages where the animals had been, and we would feed them snakes and slugs and live minnows and grasshoppers, and they would cry and beg to be let out, but we would laugh at them and stick them with sticks.

He thought of the people he hated: the park man in the city, and the Birketts' gardener who had chased him with a rake last fall when he'd caught him stealing pears, and Miss Morelli, the gym teacher at school, whose legs were too fat, and Dr. Spander, the dentist, whose hands always smelled of washing and knew how to hurt. He imagined them all in cages, all of them naked (what would Miss Morelli look like naked?), pacing and pacing frantically to and fro, the way the wild animals had done before them.

He thought of Sarah, his nurse, as she was when he hated her, when she was angry with him, hissing angry words under her breath so his mother wouldn't hear them. Not that his mother would come to his rescue if she did hear them; she was afraid of Sarah herself. He knew that. Sometimes he thought he hated her, too, but he would not put her in a cage. And even Sarah . . . At night when he woke screaming and she came in to comfort him with her empty mouth (her teeth spent the night in a glass of water), and her hair in a braid, he loved her. He clung to her bony shoulders, and she patted him with hard brittle pats and murmured to him. "No, lovey, no, lovey, it's just a dream, just a nasty old dream . . ." And once when she was dressed up to go out, with her face different, pinker, and her going-out clothes on, something had made him say, "That's a very pretty hat," although he had not really thought the hat was pretty. He'd thought it looked timid and lopsided like a hen with a broken wing, but it had made him feel sad to think that, so he'd told her it was pretty. . . . No, he wouldn't put her in a cage.

It was too mixed up, the loving and the hating; it would be better just to have them all dead and out of the way.

We would learn to fly the airplanes, he thought, and we'd have all the money. But we wouldn't need the money. And we'd have all the soda fountains. We'd stand behind the counters and squirt the soda out of the soda thing and the syrup out of the syrup thing, and we'd dig into the big, cold ice-cream cans; we'd stick our whole heads right into them; deep caves smelling of chocolate, and maple, and strawberry, and vanilla. . . . We'd have all the candy. And we'd eat liverwurst sandwiches all the time, and baloney. We'd drink ginger ale and root beer, and smoke cigars and cigarettes if we wanted to. Sometimes we'd go into the cities and we'd go to the toy stores and walk right into them and take the things we needed. . . . We'd take all the Fourth of July things and the cowboy things and the space things and the chemical sets. And we'd go to the hardware stores and take the knives and the flashlights, and we'd have all the dogs we wanted. And then we'd come back here by the sea and we'd light the big bonfires and set off the sky rockets and Roman candles, because we'd have all the sky rockets and Roman candles in the world and there wouldn't be anybody to stop us from setting them off, either; and not one of us would ever get hurt.

Stephen clicked the cap pistol and stared at the window, seeing the huge ocean night, and the Milky Way across the sky, and against that the bursting rockets. The bonfires towered on the beach and around them stood the children staring at the sky. The sound of the surf was in their ears, and all the clocks in the world were stopped, and there was nobody left to tell them to go to bed.

We wouldn't ever quarrel, he thought. We would never fall down, or be sick, and it would never rain, but if it did rain we would sleep in a tent.

✦

The door opened and his mother came in. She came in softly on her bare feet and sat down on the edge of his bed and stroked her palm across his high, round brow and stiff ringlets. He did not look at her; his fixed blue eyes stared at the corner of light that came and went with the breathing shade. In them for an instant was reflected the bright day and then the shadow; nothing else could be seen in them.

"What are you thinking about?" said his mother. She removed the candy wrapper and took his hand in hers, where it lay unresisting, like the hand of a boy asleep. "What are you thinking about, Stephen?"

"Oh . . . nothing."

"You must be thinking about *something*," she insisted.

He sighed. "Nunh-unh. Nothing."

There was silence; she stroked his fingers, one by one, and stared at him. His face was a firmament of freckles, and his nose had a pink peeled patch across it. What was at work within him? What landscape lay behind that forehead, and what figures inhabited it? She longed to know, to reach him in some way. What do children think about, she wondered. What does this one think about, so remote and so absorbed. Her love for him was a thing that hurt her. "Darling," she said.

Politely, gently, his hand slid out of her own and retrieved the candy wrapper.

"On Monday we'll have a picnic together, shall we?" she said. "Just you and I. We'll take some root beer and sandwiches and go off on our bikes for the whole day. Shall we, Stephen?"

"Okay."

"We'll go the the Coast Guard station and see if we can find some empty cartridge cases, if you like; or maybe we'll go to the swamp at Sharon Landing and look for box turtles. How would that be?"

"Okay."

"We'll go crabbing one day, too; maybe Tuesday or Wednesday. Just you and I."

Stephen glanced at her briefly. "Flora doesn't like to clean them. She told me not to ever bring her any more crabs because it takes her so long to get all the stuff out of them. It makes her very nervous, she says."

"I don't care," his mother said recklessly. "We'll go crabbing anyway, and clean them ourselves."

He turned his head on the pillow again, back toward the window; a fine, fleeting enigmatic smile played across his lips and vanished. He lay quietly, hardly breathing. "Mummy."

"Yes, darling?"

"I think maybe if you went out now maybe I could go to sleep."

"All right, Stephen."

His mother bent down and kissed the high impervious slope of his brow. Superimposed upon the freckles there she left the print of her kiss. She liked to see it there, and laughed. "I've left my mark on you again."

Her son moved one foot very slightly, almost imperceptibly to one side, and she stood up at once, not consciously knowing why. She touched his hair again, lingeringly, and fought against the words in her mind and then said them. "I love you, my dearest." She waited for a moment, standing beside the bed. Then she turned and, humming softly, tiptoed out of the room.

Stephen rolled over on his stomach, and the cap pistol fell to the floor with a sharp clatter. He rubbed his forehead against the pillow until the blot of lipstick was smeared on the white cloth. He continued to lie on his stomach, letting one leg dangle toward the floor. Slowly he put out his tongue and licked the back of his arm which tasted nicely of salt, as he had expected. The shade sighed and flapped in its restless, hopeless way, and the hum of voices droned up out of the inner heart of the house. Stephen smiled contentedly and closed his eyes.

Pretend if they were all dead, he thought. . . .

Rex

"Dead" was the word she heard oftenest when she went back that time. Dead and died. Earl Nolan was dead, and old Ella Beavis who had made many a party dress for her in the past. Percy Horter had died, drunk, falling into the flames of his own lime kiln, and Mrs. Schultz, who had lived a life that suited her in a river cabin, fishing all day, drinking beer all night, had been found on the sand, dead of a stroke. Even Jule, who had owned the tavern and who was young, had drowned on a fishing trip. And Irma Leggett had died in childbirth. . . .

"But so many of them, I can't get over it!" Gina cried.

Rose, her cousin, shrugged philosophically.

"Most of them were older, after all. Most of them were *old!* Except for Jule and Irma they were all of them up in

174

their sixties and seventies. Earl must have been almost ninety."

"I suppose so. But still; all in such a short space of time," Gina said.

"It's not so short, you know. You haven't been back in over seven years."

"Yes, that's true."

Beyond Rose, Gina saw herself suddenly in the mirror: middle-aged. This face could still surprise her; it did not feel like hers, matronly and weary, but when she saw it unexpectedly that way she could feel a stony concurrence in herself. Yes, that's how it is, she thought. Youth goes, even from me; and for a moment she would examine the desolate fact, and all her endeavors, plans, undertakings, enthusiasms, seemed abruptly worthless like paper ornaments and ribbons tied onto some uncompromising object like a boulder or a bone. Does it get worse as it goes on, she wondered. Is this the way one feels, more and more, in age? But she knew it was not. In age as in childhood one turned to details, was comforted by details, and chose them in preference to any glimpse of the whole.

"Why are you sighing?" said Rose.

"Oh, the usual," Gina said, smiling. "Death. Age. All those questions that never get answered."

"Perhaps the answers would be worst of all," Rose said, but she didn't believe it very much. She was securely optimistic as some people are securely religious. "Just look at this day, Gina! We'll go the the river, shall we?"

The fields of the valley had reached that point in ripeness and in summer at which they looked organically alive, as the fur on cats is alive. There was the faintest bloom of haze in the hot light air, and the soft breeze stroked and turned the willows and the wheat luxuriously. One felt an answering response within oneself: a longing to caress and be caressed. But the possibility of that was over now for Gina, perhaps forever, and she resolutely turned her feelings blank. This was a skill she had just begun to learn.

"Yes, let's go to the river. I haven't swum there in—well, seven years ago it was winter—so I haven't swum there in nearly sixteen years. My God, can it be? Yes; Joan was only six or seven, and Benno was a baby. Well, tempus fugit. You remember Mamie Venn and how she always used to say that to us?"

" 'Hurry up, Rosemary, Georgina, button up your leggings, hurry up. Tempus fugit. Tempus *few*-git,' she said. I wonder whoever taught her that. Of course you've probably heard she's—"

"I know; dead," said Gina, and they both laughed. Mamie Venn had been entombed in memory for so long that the fact of her actual death seemed irrelevant.

"Oh, well, let's go. Put on your suit. Shall we walk or take the car?"

"Walk. I want to look at every single thing. I want to smell everything and taste everything: sour grass, and mint, and catnip. . . ."

The two women in bathing suits, wearing sneakers and carrying towels, walked across the downsloping pastures to the dusty back road. Rose's spaniel, Rab, snuffed and zigzagged, first in front of them and then behind.

"Isn't it queer to have the children away?" Rose said. "I wonder how many hundred times I've taken them to the river."

"It's very strange," Gina said. "The way one loses them. There's no grief; it isn't *grief*, because there they are, alive and well, but there is loss. As people they remain; as children they're gone, gone, gone. Joan can look at me with a basilisk's eye, and Benno says he's an Existentialist. I liked it better when he was a Martian."

"I know. One misses them. Toy stores depress me, especially. Well, someday there'll be grandchildren, thank goodness."

"I wish I were like you, an optimist."

"Yes, I know, I'm very lucky," Rose said complacently, as one who accepts praise for a fine complexion or the possession of true pitch.

They turned from the road and crawled beneath a line of barbed-wire fence.

"Ouch. How easy this used to be," Rose said, groaning mildly as she got to her feet.

The pasture—the last pasture they were to cross—was just as Gina remembered it from her childhood: cropped bare except for the rejected weeds. Vervain and mullein stood tall and intact, and in a hollow there was the sweet tangle of prickly ash and honeysuckle that had grown there forever.

The trees by the river were the same: one leaning exhaustedly on a branch bent like an elbow, one with two trunks wrapped in an embrace. And the river was as she remembered it, or almost as she remembered it; each year for reasons beyond her comprehension it shifted its currents one way or another, exposing new beaches or creating new islands. It had always done this, and some summers it lay low between its banks and flowed quietly, and some summers it was deep and hurried in spots, with erratic eddies and pockets of danger.

This year it was low. They crossed the mossy edge of the pasture and waded through a yellow backwater to the sand, which was pitted and trampled, and scattered with gaping clamshells like discarded purses. To the left, a great shoulder of limestone cast its shadow on olive-colored water.

"I smell this river and I'm ten years old again," Gina said.

They walked out of the warm shadow of the bluff into the hot sunlight of the strand. Across the next river bend there was a vessel-shaped island in full sail. Its poplars and cottonwoods quivered their ten thousand leaves, and somewhere among them a cicada began its red-hot drilling.

The water between the strand and the island was shallow, no higher than their knees as they waded through it. Rab splashed ahead of them, sending up fountains of iridescent spray.

The island had a skirt of yellow sand, traced over and over with marks of claws and mice feet. Straight as leaves on a stem, a heron's prints crossed it to the other shore. There, the river was deeper, and it was there that they would swim.

But first they sat down, yawning and relaxed, rubbing sunburn lotion on their skin.

"Oh, what a lovely, lovely place," Gina said. "How could I have stayed away so long?"

"You'll be free to come here oftener now."

"Yes," Gina said, but she thought "free" was a queer word to use.

"Oh, look, Rab's got another turtle. It's all he ever catches. He's a turtle retriever, that's what you are, aren't you, Rab? Come here, give it to me!"

The wet spaniel trotted to her holding the turtle in his mouth like a club sandwich. He looked smiling and proud.

"He wouldn't dream of tackling anything as vicious as a rabbit, would you, darling? *That's* my good dog," said Rose, relieving him of the turtle and turning it over in her hands. "Why Gina—Gina, look! There's a name carved on its shell. 'Rex,' it says, and there's a date." She held it away from her to see better. " '1939.' Twenty-five years ago! And it was probably full-grown when he carved it, whoever he was. This is an elderly turtle, Gina; I wish I were as well preserved."

"Let me see," Gina held out her hand and took the turtle; smooth, neither warm nor cool.

"I wonder which Rex it was, though," Rose said. "Rex Baumeister? Rex McCarten? Rex Hauser? There was a rash of Rexes in the valley then, just as there was a rash of Joannes."

"Rex Wharton," Gina said remotely.

"Oh, Rex Wharton! How could I have forgotten him—the way he looked then . . . Do you remember him in the fields, riding the tractor? Blue jeans and no shirt—his back and chest and shoulders burned reddish-bronze. I never saw a color like it."

And his hair, Gina thought, sun-bleached till it was almost white, almost a blinding white.

"Like Phaëton with the horses of Apollo, I used to think."

"Except it was Corby Forgan's old Oliver tractor. I'm going for a dip—are you coming?"

"Later."

Gina had put the turtle on the sand, and now it thrust out its angry old man's head and its flat thorned feet and started toward the water. She reached out and plucked it back again. At once the head and feet were sullenly retracted. She held it on her palm, tracing the carved letters it had worn so long on its stone back.

Rex. Rex Wharton. He was a secret in her mind that no one else had ever guessed.

She had known him in her childhood, though he was older, the friend of Rose's brother: a tow-headed farm boy, gentle and good-natured. She had liked him vaguely, never knowing him well.

Then came a summer of drought, when streams shrank, the corn plants rattled in bone-dry fields, and nothing washed the heavy road powder from the wayside weeds. It was a hard year for farmers. But to Gina, sixteen years old, just home from school, each merciless day was only another sunny day: something to rejoice in. Rex Wharton had turned into Phaëton since the summer before, but at first she didn't notice that.

She and Rose and their friends had used the river like otters, day and night—the boys joined them after work—and sometimes, when there was a moon, they canoed all the way to the

Melody Dancing Ranch, where the music was terrible—but who cared?—and often they took picnics to the river bank or to some island. She remembered the fireflies, like green eyes slowly opening and closing; the tinny nagging of mosquitoes— all of them, all the young people, smelled of citronella that summer and sometimes the sandwiches tasted of it.

And then one night, after the fireflies had gone and the crickets had started, so it must have been August, they had been on another picnic. There had been the songs, the jokes, the pairings off into the darkness, and finally the time to go home. She and Rex had lagged behind the others—not saying much; they never had had much to say. They walked cautiously and slowly through the dung-studded pasture. The night was dense, windless; toward the west the heat lightning fanned and shuddered, but overhead the stars were large and steady. The lightning would come to nothing and so would the soft restless thunder. The warm night was more private, more enclosing, than the walls of a room, Gina thought. She turned to look at Rex, his blond head faintly glimmering, and it was then, at that very moment, that the change took place, as though a continuing sound had altered in tone; deepened without warning. One moment Rex was Rex, and in the next he was a mystery, and she was in love.

He felt it, too, and took her hand. They stopped walking. He dropped whatever it was he'd been carrying, put both his hands on her waist, stepped close to her, pressed against her, and then they were kissing. Those were her first real kisses, and she remembered very well the transformation from the stiffness of embarrassment, of being too new at something, to the revelation of sense; and then the participation.

It had gone on like that all summer—what was left of the summer—and for her, at least, the kisses were enough.

She had never seen him again. She'd gone back to school, to Europe, to college, to the living of her own life. She had had one letter from him, only one, inarticulate, unsatisfying, though she'd written him a dozen; and for a period of months she had suffered, believing her heart to be broken; as indeed it was, for the time being.

"The heart's a tough old thing, though; as tough as you are," she said to the turtle. The pain had vanished years and years ago; all that endured was a certain gratitude to Rex for the knowing, tender role he'd played in her initiation.

Rose came dripping from the river.

"It's not cold enough to be bracing, but it's better than nothing," she said, scattering drops and reaching for a towel.

"Did he ever marry?" Gina asked.

"Who?"

"Rex Wharton."

"Oh. Wait till I tell you! Yes, he did."

Rose lowered herself to the sand.

"He married Cordelia Volker. I don't think you ever knew her; she came from Pickrel Point. You wouldn't remember her anyway. She was mousy and toothy, a quiet little thing. But she wore sweaters and her breasts were very pointed: they looked alert and inquisitive, like the noses of twin fox terriers. You couldn't ignore them; no *boy* could. There began to be some queer stories about her. . . ."

"And *that's* who Rex married? When?" Gina let the turtle walk a little way, then seized him back again.

"Ages ago. Do you remember the summer of the drought when all the farmers suffered so, and we had so much fun?"

"Yes."

"Well, it was sometime during the winter after that. Late in the winter. All of a sudden Rex and Cordelia went to Chicago and came back married. No one had even guessed that there was anything between them, and a lot of girls took it hard. *They'd* seen him being Phaëton in the summertime."

So he was good at keeping secrets, too, Gina thought. The turtle lay like a closed clam in her hand.

"Then the rumors ran their usual course: that he'd had to marry her, and so on. They always say that in a place like this; and it was true Rex didn't look what you'd call radiant. But he was a wonderfully well-disposed, kind person in spite of being handsome. You remember that about him, don't you?"

"Yes," Gina said.

"He did his best to make the marriage go. He was sweet and considerate always. But his bride had pointed little teeth (as well as breasts) that looked as if she'd been sharpening them on birch twigs all her life. And her words were sharp—to Rex, and about him. She soon turned out to be a nagger. Perhaps she knew he didn't love her; and events proved that he *hadn't* had to marry her after all. Her waistline, carefully and covertly observed, never changed its twenty-two-inch span. We were always sure she'd tricked him.

"Then there was the war and he was gone. Four years in the Pacific. Cordelia took a job in the bank, and often on weekends she went to Milwaukee or Chicago. People ran into her now and then, always with some man. She'd taken a room for herself in the village; she hated farm life, and she wasn't very friendly with Rex's father. I think she thought he was below her on the social scale. *He* didn't care; you remember what a darling he was?"

"That enormous man, always working, always laughing. He seemed so much a part of this valley I thought he'd live forever," Gina said.

"He didn't though. He began to shrink away, and dwindle, but he managed to hold on till Rex came home, and then he died.

"Rex, of course, inherited the farm; it was his to work, but not for long. It wasn't Cordelia's cup of tea at all. So she whinnied and niggled and made life hell till he gave in, sold the farm, and put his money into a motel: the Cord-Rex Court Motel five miles outside the village on the highway.

"They did quite well for several years but then the picture changed entirely. The state pushed through the Plains Expressway seven miles to the north—and there was the Cord-Rex Motel slumped by a dead issue of a road. Two much bigger, glossier motor courts reared up beside the throughway and took away the business. A few people came to the Cord-Rex, but not many. Rex opened up a store then, a sort of general store, in the hope of attracting business in that way. I used it often, though it was inconvenient; a lot of us did, just because of Rex, but even so . . .

"And then *Cordelia's* father died and her mother had to come and live with them. You should have seen her, Gina! Chins giving way to chins; a riot of fat. When she walked she creaked and buckled like a damaged carnival balloon. She and Cordelia didn't get on. Cordelia snapped at her all the time, and she—she was too fat to snap—she rumbled and honked back at her daughter; and both of them let Rex have it. Oh, it was a merry household; Ethan Frome wasn't in it! There were no children, no dog, no cat; but there *was* a certain traveling salesman—"

"Why did Rex *stand* for such a life?"

"Perhaps because he wasn't very used to women—family women, that is. He'd had no mother since he was three or four—no sisters. Only that dim, elderly aunt that came to live with them—and then, sweet though he was, and admirable, I'm afraid he wasn't very brilliant—"

"Beautiful, though."

"You should have seen him when he came back from the Pacific! But in a very short time—working like a dog, hardly ever out of doors, constantly chivied by the birch-biter and the honking balloon—he began to fade. You know how it is when you catch some tropical fish—a Caribbean dolphin, for instance—how iridescent it is? Life makes light all over its skin, and then as it dies the light fades, the color goes and there's nothing to look at any more. Rex was like that—all the brightness leached away."

Gina put the turtle on the sand. She watched its wary emergence, its cautious try for escape. She let it walk a little farther this time before she reached out and caught it.

"So that's the way it went: from bad to worse. The store failed: one of those big trumpeting shopping centers had opened up. Rex got a job there, part time, that he hated, and the Cord-Rex limped along in a halfhearted way. The traveling salesman came oftener and stayed longer.

"And then one day he disappeared."

"The traveling salesman?"

"Rex, silly!"

Gina looked up, clasping the turtle.

"*Rex* disappeared?"

"They found his clothes on the riverbank, and that was all."

"Oh, no, oh, no!"

"His clothes and shoes, neatly arranged, just this side of the bridge. And there, if you remember, the river is always deep and treacherous, even in dry summers.

"So they dragged the river and the pools and searched the riverbanks from here to Boscobel, but never a trace did they find. . . . More than one of us thought it was suicide, and all of us mourned him: he was such a patient, good person who'd deserved better of life. All of us mourned him but one, and maybe she did, too, in some dark tortuous little way of her own. In any case she very soon perked up and began to revamp the Cord-Rex. She got a liquor license, for one thing (borrowed the money from her gentleman friend, I imagine), and a couple of jukeboxes. People began to go there again— certain people—and then she settled down to bide her time till

Rex was officially declared dead, and she could collect his life insurance, and get married again. . . ."

"To the traveling salesman?"

"No, to the bartender. He beats her up from time to time and keeps her fairly happy."

"Oh, God, but poor Rex!"

"Now wait. A few years ago when I went to Mexico—I wrote you, remember?—the Spencers, Draco and Virginia, took me fishing in the Gulf of California—far, far down the coast. I loved it. We stayed at a fishing lodge each night, and started out early every morning in a beat-up old cabin cruiser. I fished some of the time; sometimes I just sat and lived.

"Morning is the whole meaning of the day down there: the apotheosis of morning. The atmosphere is burning, pared of blur, of any kind of vagueness. The islands are brusque and pinnacled, but there are little beaches, too; bitten in sharply. The whole thing is sharp, fierce, magnificent. . . .

"Every day we rocked about between those islands. The crewmen, both of them, were Mexican. They had no English, we had hardly any Spanish. It didn't matter; fish bite in any language. At least down there. The sea teems with life: big, rowing turtles . . ."

(Gina glanced at the resigned one in her hand.)

". . . mantas hopping out like crazy kites, a sea lion floating on his back with his toe-flippers sticking up. All he needed was a cigar. . . . Oh, I loved it!"

"I can see you did," Gina said, a little dryly.

"All right. End of travelogue. . . . So one afternoon we neared another island, where a boat was beached. Virginia was in the cabin taking a siesta; Draco was taking an unofficial one, in his chair, nodding over his rod: Mexican beer and Mexican light had done their work. I was drowsy myself.

"The boat drew nearer to the island. No one in sight, until suddenly along the shore a little boy came running: apricot-colored, with hair like bleached straw—startling in that land of dark-haired, dark-eyed people, startling on that empty shore. . . . He stopped, waved, called out in Spanish to the crewmen, and they called back. Softly, not to spoil the two siestas.

"Then rounding a pinnacle of rock a man and woman came in sight, walking hand in hand—we were close to the shore. The woman was young, a girl, dark and pretty. And the man—her husband—was Rex."

"Oh, it couldn't be! Rose! It was one of those freak like-nesses—"

"It was Rex, Gina. It was Rex, with all the light restored to him. Older, of course, but with that brightness he used to have, and burned by the sun to the color we remember . . ."

"How on earth can you be sure?"

"Wait. He called a greeting to the sailors, too. Then he saw me; we were close. He looked straight at me, Gina, and then—I don't think anybody saw it, or if they did they didn't under-stand it; it was just for me—he put his finger to his lips: the smallest gesture, and I nodded my head twice, very slightly, just for him. It was my promise to him, and I've kept it faith-fully; until today."

"But how was he there? Why? What was he *doing?*"

"I never knew. I never asked. He must have learned a great deal about the sea and boats and navigation all those years in the Pacific. Perhaps he'd become a fishing guide—or a plain fisherman—perhaps he'd made a lot of money and was vaca-tioning, as we were—who knows? And I really didn't want to know. It was like an episode in a dream, isolated from cause and effect. Simply there. There he was, entirely out of con-text, and I saw no clue to tell me anything. He was in blue jeans, barefoot, and she was pregnant, wearing some dark thing, and barefoot, too. There was nothing to indicate their fortunes. Nothing to see except that brilliant little running boy, and Rex with all the brightness back."

Gina was quiet for a moment; then she said: "How nice to hear surprising news that someone is alive, instead of always just the other. Eerie, though."

"Eerie, yes. But in my memory the vivid light, the child, the man and woman, the rocks—they're like a drawing, or a thought, of Blake's. And satisfying. All I wanted to know, I saw."

"You're wise, Rose. Even if you are an optimist."

Holding the turtle, Gina got to her feet, ready to swim. Halfway to the water, she turned to her cousin.

"Then what's-her-name, Cordelia, is really living in sin!"

"In bigamy. They both are. And no one knows but me. And now you."

"I am excellent at keeping secrets," Gina said. "It's the only virtue I have that I'm sure of."

She walked into the river slowly; it was no cooler than the air, only the element was different. She waded out till the water clasped her waist where Rex's hands had clasped it once.

She dipped the turtle in the water and let it go, watched it—an oval shadow disappearing.

"Run away, Rex, run away. Escape from the tyrant," Gina said; then she leaned into the bland water and began to swim where she had swum so often in her youth.

A Distant Bell

The year after my father and mother were divorced, my
father, who got me in the summers, took me to a town on the
Cape called Harbor Landing. It was a fish-smelling, gull-
squeaking, heterogeneous sort of town heaped up on the hills
and bluffs that commanded a view of the harbor with its
fringe of docks and shanties. Artists swarmed there in the
summertime.

The name of our hotel was "The Nippanoggin Inn." The
name was the jauntiest thing about it; indeed it was the only
jaunty thing. The clapboarded building was painted egg-yolk
yellow and had a mansard roof. The tiers of porches on the
harbor side were stocked with wooden rocking chairs that
rocked untenanted when the east wind blew, and that summer
they rocked often.

"All right, Susie, this is yours, right next to mine," my father said, as if his hearty tone could liven up the room he led me into. Through the two windows facing me I saw the gray, littered harbor. The scrim curtains were limp and blotched with liver spots of rust, and looped on a hook beside the right-hand window there was a coil of knotted rope.

"What's that thing for?" I said, unbuttoning my coat.

"Well, *not* to hang yourself with, Sue! Quite the opposite. That's your own personal fire escape. But I'm certain you won't need to use it unless you're planning to elope."

My father, I sensed, was trying hard. I smiled obligingly, though I thought he could not know much about me if he didn't know I loathed most boys and planned never to marry; and it was no joking matter. I was eleven years old, with straight red hair, and skinny knees that jutted out above my socks. I felt uncomfortable with my father, and I think he did with me. We did not know each other very well, having lost track of each other, rather, in the years just past.

"Well, I hope you're going to be comfortable here, Susie. It's not what I'd call . . . it's not a luxurious bower exactly. But then we'll be outdoors a lot," he said, brightening. "Now why don't you unpack, get settled? I will, too, and then we'll go out and explore the town, shall we?"

"All right," I said.

When he had gone I went to the iron bedstead and sat down. The mattress felt as if it had been stuffed with the unclaimed laundry of former guests. I examined my new furniture: bureau, washstand, small lame table by the window. There were two chairs; my father had put my suitcase on one of them, and instead of a closet there was a cretonne curtain that hung from a rod at one side of the room. I supposed that by the time I returned to the city all these things would have become familiar and accepted, a sort of home, but it was hard to believe just then.

I got up and opened my suitcase and took out the reading material that lay on my folded clothes: a copy of *John Martin's Book*, a copy of the *Atlantic Monthly*. One by one I lifted out my dresses and hung them on the jangling hangers behind the curtain. When I was putting my underclothes into a bureau drawer I caught sight of my face in the mirror.

"Hideous mule," I said to it, and then leaned forward with interest to watch as a tear rolled slowly down one cheek.

There was a knock at the door. I hastily disposed of the tear with a pair of socks, and turned to face my father.

He looked greatly refreshed, and there was a whiff of something new about him: a whiff of something to drink, I thought. I was glad. If he felt better, then I felt better, too.

The town was remarkably ugly, I remember that. Ugly in spite of the elms, in spite of the fine old houses, in spite of the harbor. It was ugly with people. At that time of day the trippers from Boston, with their celluloid visors and boat-burned faces and paper bags and cameras and children, poured into the main street. All their faces were in motion as they talked, laughed, ogled, jeered, and, dipping things out of the brown paper bags, chewed, gobbled, sucked, and spat out pits. All their eyes roved and darted eagerly, looking for artists, for the outlandish (and perhaps scandalous?) artists they had come to see; and the artists obliged. Not only had they left their traces everywhere, palette-knife scrapings on elm bark and curbstone and fence picket, but they were themselves boldly in evidence. Sporting sandals and beards, Navajo necklaces and earrings like buckets, they walked along the street in loud groups or sat at their easels in full view, together or alone, painting the same outpainted wharves, boats, and old characters that had been their subjects for years; but painting them, now, with a difference.

"Don't look like no boat to me, looks more like my grammother's flatiron," remarked an onlooker, ramming peanuts into his mouth, as his boiled-red wife shook with laughter and shifted the baby to her other hip.

More and more people clogged the street.

"Let's get out of this. They may stampede," my father said. He took my hand and tucked it in his arm and we plowed a course through the crowd, turned down a side street, and came to the harbor. It was low tide, and the exposed marly sand was studded with shells and bits of interesting trash. I picked up an old tin fork and a piece of green bottle glass.

"We'll find the bathing beach tomorrow," my father promised.

That night after dinner he produced a parcheesi board and we had a long satisfying game which I won. Afterward when I lay down on my remarkable mattress I fell asleep at once and slept for eleven hours, and when I woke up the windows were full of sun.

My father and I were alike in this way; we didn't care for talk at breakfast time. My mother was the opposite; she would begin to burble like a house wren the moment she opened her eyes. But now, alone with my father, I sat in silence reading while I ate, a habit I was never allowed to indulge at home. My father allowed it because he wanted to read himself; the arrangement suited us both.

During the morning he worked in his room, and I would sit at my little lame table painting pictures of sorceresses and queens. When I looked out of the window I saw the harbor, the fussy boats, the swinging gulls. Next door I could hear the clacking of the typewriter, sometimes hurried and voluble; sometimes hesitant. There would be a long exasperated pause, a tentative tap and tap-tap, another pause, then sometimes the sound of an exclamation and the dry crumpling of paper.

At noon he would knock on my door and we went off to swim at the bathing beach where the water was clean and dazzling. He was an excellent swimmer, my father, and liked to swim well out and away from the shore. I used to watch with real anxiety as his head and rhythmically flailing arms grew more and more distant, were nearly lost to view. I could not settle down to my enjoyment until he had returned from that first long sortie into the blue.

"Don't worry about me, Sue," he said. "I always turn back as soon as I see Spain."

He told me of creatures he had met along the way: the plaice fish who gave him tips on the horses. "Sea horses, that is," he said; and the jellyfish named Mrs. Cadwallader, "a Main Line jellyfish. But she can't find a corset to fit her."

He made short shrift of my formless side stroke and spent hours teaching me the crawl and the trudgen; accomplishments I cherish to this day.

It was always rather late when we returned to the inn. Sometimes they had run out of corn on the cob. The other occupants of the dining room, mostly in aging pairs, bowed chewing above their plates. The stained-glass clerestory above sent down a churchly light, and imposed a churchly hush. We spoke in low tones.

"Southern fried chicken," grumbled my father, sawing away at a drumstick. "Southern fried buzzard, more likely. Southern fried emu."

Besides the chicken there was always roast beef *au jus* on the menu, and Boston scrod. The beef was served in green-gray slices chilled at the edges, and I could never bring myself to try anything called scrod. The vegetables came in little extra dishes: succotash awash in milk, potatoes mashed with water and flung onto the dish with a ladle.

"Thank God for catsup," my father used to say; but I did not care for catsup. I was perfectly happy, though, on my diet of bread and butter and milk and ice cream.

"I don't suppose I ought to allow it," my father said helplessly. "Don't they . . . doesn't your mother make you eat everything at home?"

"Oh, they can't *make* me, Daddy," I assured him. "I have the appetite of a bird."

When he didn't go back to work we spent the afternoons together; going on expeditions in the little roadster he had hired, walking along the ocean shore where surf gnawed the beaches, or searching in the pine woods for Indian pipes. When he played golf I walked the course with him and was his caddy.

And I had found a friend for the days when he was busy: a girl named Avalon Bray who lived near the beach. She was two years older than I was, and in certain ways seemed older than that; I noticed that she looked at any boys we saw with a worried, wistful glance. As yet the boys did not respond. Avalon wore braces on her teeth that looked like lead, her hair was a mess, and she had not "filled out"; instead she looked *pulled* out, as if she had just recently been stretched from something smaller.

Still, she was a companion, and we spent hours playing in the sea together, or wandering on the tide flats that smelled of chowder and crackled with the occupations of crabs.

"Gee, Sue, I think your father's *cute!*" she startled me by saying, one day.

"Cute? Men can't be cute," I said.

"Sure they can. Some. *He* is. He's *good*-looking."

I knew that. It was strange. I could not tell whether my mother was pretty or not; her face was simply Mother's Face. But I knew my father was handsome, and could see it.

At night, after dinner, he and I played our games, parcheesi or dominoes, and sometimes, if I begged him, he would tell me a story as he had often done when I was younger. He was very good at this and could spin a story out to last for hours.

I went to bed late those nights, and often the last thing I heard before I slept was the irregular castanet-note of his typewriter.

All those days were fair. I remember them as being fair. The weather changed when Mrs. Fenwick came: the morning of the day she came.

When I woke up that day the east wind was blowing; the window curtains tossed listlessly, and the noise of gulls was sharp in the room. At breakfast my father was even more silent than usual. Perhaps the weather and the constant companionship of an eleven-year-old daughter were beginning to chafe his spirits.

His work went badly that morning; I could tell by the silences. The rain began to spit at ten; and I upset a jar of crimson madder on the rug.

At lunch he was morose. The vegetable was spinach. "Or is it kelp?" he wondered; and he said his coffee tasted as if there were limpets in it.

Afterward he returned to work, and I went to Avalon's house, which was wracked with the noise of younger brothers. We locked ourselves in her room with a supply of graham crackers and peanut butter, and she told me the facts of life.

"My heavens, Sue, you mean you honestly didn't *know?*"

"Not quite. Not exactly," I admitted, fascinated and appalled. Could I believe her, or was she crazy?

"Oh, my heavens, you're such a *baby!*" she cried, suddenly exasperated by my youth. With this beginning we managed a quarrel, and soon I left the house, upset on several counts.

At the inn I found my father in the lobby reading the paper.

"Couldn't stand that damned room another second," he said. "And I think the typewriter has rabies. It bit me. Where's what's-her-name? Avalon?"

"Oh, we're mad."

"What about?"

"Oh, nothing much," I said, glad of a sudden stir at the outer entrance of the lobby.

Calvin, the elderly bellboy, hobbled in with a load of Vuitton luggage. Behind him came two women, two new guests. One of them was old, stooped and tremulous, but the other, on whose arm she was leaning, was tall and commanding. She gave an immediate effect of confidence, perhaps accentuated by the contrast between herself and her companion. She also gave an effect of luxury, of well-being; all her appurtenances seemed exactly right for her: the fur scarf, the large hat with a veil, the big pearls on her ear lobes, and most of all the soft expensive aura of perfume that breathed from her.

"You sit down here, Auntie," she said to the older woman. "I'll sign the register." Her voice was rich and confident, too. I thought of the word *contralto*, although I was not certain of its meaning.

"Daddy," I said. "It's stopped raining. Can we go over to the surf now? Daddy? Can we?"

Though he stood facing me, my father was looking intently from the corners of his eyes at the tall woman signing the register. He did not answer.

"Daddy!" I repeated sharply.

At this the tall woman turned suddenly and looked over her shoulder at me, at him. She smiled a warm, friendly smile at me, at him. The fur stole slipped from her shoulders to the floor, and my father sprang forward.

"Oh, thank you so much! How clumsy of me!"

My father bowed and smiled, then turned to me lightheartedly. "All right, Mrs. Murphy, what do you say we go for a spin?" This was a name he called me when he was feeling cheerful.

In the dining room that evening, we saw that the newcomers

had a table near the door. The tall one greeted us as we went by, and I noticed that my father glanced in her direction more than once during the meal.

Afterward, though the air was gray and damp, we went through the lounge to the veranda, as we did every evening. My father liked to smoke there after dinner.

He took a cigar from his pocket and clipped the end; absently he slipped the cigar band off and handed it to me. "Here's the ring you ordered, Mrs. Murphy."

I took it but did not put it on my finger. Cigar-band rings were for people of seven or less; I had finished with them years ago.

There was a sound of women's voices in the lounge, and I knew who was coming because of the smell of perfume that came first.

The tall woman held the screen door open for her aunt.

"I hope we're not disturbing you?"

"Of course not!" said my father quickly, standing up. He moved two rockers to the rail near ours, then introduced himself and me.

"And I am Meta Fenwick," she said. "Mrs. Abel Fenwick. And this is my aunt, Miss Currier."

We all sat down, Miss Currier taking a while to settle, cocooning herself against the damp; requiring a cushion from the lounge. Her niece opened a beaded bag and took out a cigarette case. Gold. And in it were flat little cigarettes with golden tips.

"I didn't think they'd care to have me smoking in the lounge!" she confided, smiling at my father. "But I simply must have my cigarette after dinner. I am an addict!"

My father held a light for her; and soon there was another smoke to mingle with his: light, musky, rather sweet. I left my rocker and sat on the rail so I could watch her better.

"Honey, don't you *fall*," said Mrs. Fenwick, but not as if she were really worried; just to be polite.

She was an ample woman, not fat or plump, but *ample*. She was tall, as I have said, with a large bosom, and a creamy skin. Her gray eyes were long and luminous, her glossy hair was marcelled under a hair net, and there was a deep dimple in her chin. She laughed as often as she did, I suspect, because her teeth were flawless; and how well I remember that laugh! It had an easy, gratified quality. Everything about her was smooth, luxurious, unhurried.

Examining my memory of her I can see, now, that she was dead ripe: a woman at the last perfect moment before the gray begins in the hair and the soft flesh becomes a little too soft. . . . It surprises me that I hated her so soon. She did her best to win me; she was kind, and I was not often given to hatred.

After that evening nothing was the same again. On the few days when we could swim, Mrs. Fenwick swam with us. She was a good golfer, too, so most of my father's afternoons were spent with her on the course; and now when we played our evening games there were three of us; sometimes four, though Miss Currier had become, as such old ladies often do, a background type.

("Poor Auntie, she's had so little. I'm all the family she has left. And she is all that I have . . . now."

"Your husband?" murmured my father.

"I've been a widow for three years," she told him gently.)

So I spent more and more time with Avalon. We had patched our quarrel up as we patched up many others. Our quarrels were not important; but neither was our friendship. We were nothing to each other but a means of killing time. Avalon, especially, was restive; she longed to be off and away in the next exciting part of life. All of her was ready for it but her looks, poor thing. My childishness must have been a constant reminder and goad to her.

One day we took a picnic (with Mrs. Fenwick) to a place called Kettle Cove. Avalon went with us. All of us swam, but she and I kept on till we were sodden, as we always did. It was noon when we came out. Mrs. Fenwick and my father lay propped on their elbows on the sand, talking in low voices.

"Look at them," whispered Avalon, giving me a jab. "Your father's got a case on her, they've got a case on each *other*. Anyone can tell." She giggled, and suddenly, against my will, I thought of the things she had told me in her room that day.

"Oh, they have not. You're dis*gus*ting! Go to hell!" I whispered furiously. But we had to sacrifice that quarrel; after all, we were stuck there for the day, and with them.

As we got out of the car at the inn I heard Mrs. Fenwick murmur to my father: "We don't care what the tabbies in the rocking chairs are saying, do we?"

That evening she came out on the veranda to smoke her cigarette, wrapped in a pale-blue cashmere coat.

"Autumn is in the air," my father said.

"Yes, too soon . . . It always comes too soon." She looked at me perched on the railing, trying not to shiver. "Why, Susie dear, your teeth are chattering. Come here, come under my wing."

She held out the edges of her coat and a warm gust of perfume came from her. Half fascinated, half repelled, I allowed myself to be drawn into this shelter and stood there rigidly, conscious of the soft bosom and the breath behind it, and the perfume. Her arms and her coat were warm around me. For some reason I thought suddenly and longingly of a boy at home named Raymond Trout, who could walk on his

hands, and spit like a man. I remembered his voice in the twilight shouting, "All-ee, all-ee in free!"

"Relax, you little giraffe," Mrs. Fenwick said teasingly.
"Really, Howard—" ("Howard," I thought!) "Your daughter
feels just as bony and on guard as a little captured giraffe."

I hated her for that, too; for the first time I felt as Avalon
must feel: that I was an unfinished product, ridiculous for this
reason, as goslings, half-grown cats, and colts are, having lost
their infancy's appeal and not yet having gained the authority
of being grown.

So for this, and for calling my father "Howard," I knew at
last how much I hated Mrs. Fenwick, and freed myself from
her embrace.

"I'd rather go and get my sweater," I said brusquely.

"You'd better go and get in bed if you can't be more
polite," my father chided.

But now it was impossible to be polite to Mrs. Fenwick.
When she begged me not to chew the stalks of beach grass
because she had heard of a child who had died of anthrax from
doing this, I skipped before her along the path, pulling stalks
and chewing them defiantly. When she invited me to go to the
movies I said that movies gave me a headache, and when she
offered me candy I said I wasn't hungry. Both lies. Sometimes she brought me presents, and while I accepted them
(they were good presents), it was all I could do to thank her.

"She is a lovely person," my father said, and though the
words weren't spoken as a question, I knew that he desired an
answer, and I gave none.

They were always together, and I tagged along. In the evenings they sat on the veranda long after I had gone to bed. I
never heard the typewriter now, as I went off to sleep. Sometimes we would go down to the deserted "ballroom" in the

basement where there was a piano. It was afflicted with a seaside twang, but she would play on it and sing in German or English. When she sang in English she pronounced the words as trained singers do; to me they sounded elegant, distorted, and embarrassing. But my father looked as though he could not hear enough, or watch enough.

Summer was nearly over. We were to leave Harbor Landing on the last day of August, while Mrs. Fenwick and her aunt planned to stay through Labor Day. "It will only be a week," she said to my father, and he said: "That week will have too many days in it."

But on the twenty-ninth Mrs. Fenwick had an unexpected visitor: a gentleman who arrived in a white Wills-St. Clair roadster with the top down. He had a red-bronze sunburn, and in the gray hair that rippled back from his forehead there was a glimpse of red-bronze bald spot. His gray mustache was twisted with wax into a little quill at each corner.

"Why, *Carroll!*" cried Mrs. Fenwick, when she saw him. "How on earth—why didn't you let me *know?* You never *said—*"

"I wanted to surprise you! I'm on my way to Bar Harbor"—"Bah Habbah," he called it—"to stop with the Murrays for Labor Day. So I thought, I'll just take a detour"—"daytaw," he called it—"and spend a few days with Meta."

I saw the way his fingers slid up and down the inside of her smooth arm; and I saw her draw the arm away.

"Aren't you glad to see me?"

"Of course, Carroll. Surprised, that's all. You startled me."

I didn't think she cared for her surprise, and when she introduced the man, Mr. Bailey, to my father, it was the first time I had ever seen her look uncomfortable, not in command. My father must have noticed it. I saw his eyes go from her face to Mr. Bailey's and back to hers. After a minute of talking he put his hand on my shoulder.

"Beach time, Sue. Go get your things."

Mrs. Fenwick and her friend were not in the dining room for lunch that day. They were not there for dinner. Alone at the table, Miss Currier picked daintily and ravenously at her food.

My father and I sat in the lounge to play our evening games, and every time someone entered or went past the door he looked up quickly. "Daddy, you're not paying *attention!*" I said. I was winning all the games, but it was not fun to win them this way.

Mr. Bailey did not stay for his "few days" after all. He left early the next morning, and no one saw him off. Calvin the bellboy told me that.

My father had promised, on this last day, to take Avalon and me for a picnic at a lighthouse twenty miles away.

"But isn't Mrs. Fenwick coming?" I asked him.

"No," he said, and slammed the car door firmly.

That day was flawless, and at the end of it Avalon and I had our good-byes. "You write me now, Susie!"

"Oh, I will, and you write me! Promise?"

"I promise."

We knew that we would never write.

As we went in to dinner that night I noticed that though my father smiled and greeted Mrs. Fenwick and her aunt, he did not stop to speak to them as he usually did. I skipped gaily to my place and ate an enormous dinner.

Afterward we had the veranda to ourselves; it was too damp for everyone but us. Fog had come smoking in from the sea, milky, and so dense that it collected on the eaves and dripped from them. Far, far away the harbor buoy tolled on the lifting tide.

"It's the last time," I said mournfully, for though I was not very fond of that veranda I had a superstitious regard for leave-takings. My father did not reply. He smoked in silence, and I forbore to rock my chair.

Behind us the screen door opened, closed. There was a smell of perfume in the air. My father stood up.

"Good evening," he said, severely.

She came and stood before him wearing her blue cashmere coat. She did not need to touch him with her hand; she used her voice.

"Howard," she said. "Howard?"

I understood her tone. It was one I sometimes used myself, pleading for something I wanted very badly. Hoping for something.

"Susie, it's your bedtime," my father said.

I was outraged. "It is *not!*"

"You have packing to do, I think."

"I have *not*. It's done."

Mrs. Fenwick took my hand in hers, a full, smooth hand; I snatched my own away.

"Susie, dear. Honey. Forgive me, will you? I want to talk to your father, may I? Alone? Just for a little while?"

"Scat, Susie," said my father, and then, more kindly: "I'm sure you have some things to do. We won't be long."

I wasn't a baby. I couldn't howl and clutch the railing. I left without a word. As I went through the lounge I looked back and saw his arm come up around her shoulders.

My father was wrong; I had no "things to do." My suitcase was packed; my traveling clothes were ready. The room was bare and tidy, home no longer, and through the window came the sound of the far bell.

I told myself they wouldn't mind if I went back to the lounge, where there were magazines to read. How could they mind that? Still, I tiptoed as I crossed the varnished floor to the magazine table. The lounge was deserted except for an old man in a chair, asleep and puffing softly.

Fog muffled the town noises, but the bell came clear, and the voices of the two on the veranda were a steady murmur. Hers, then his, then hers again. I turned the pages of a *National Geographic* and studied the pictures of a Dyak family, all with large stomachs.

"No!" said my father loudly from the porch.

Her voice rose, too. "But, Howard, honestly! What did you think . . . what can you expect? . . . I am not a nun!"

"But *that* fellow . . . how you could *bring* yourself—"

Her voice murmured and murmured, then rose again: "I thought we could be honest with each other. I really did. I thought we *should* be . . ."

"But that fellow. That tin-plate Percy Millionbucks. My God!"

Murmur, murmur, from her; then his voice gruff and abrupt. I had heard voices like these before, in my own house, when they thought I was asleep. Hers came up again.

". . . didn't suppose that you'd be pleased, but this boorish jealousy . . . I never would have imagined, I never would have *dreamed*—"

"Very well. All right, I'm a boor. But there's a name I could call you, too, you know, Meta!"

I heard her gasp, and I knew she stood up suddenly: her rocker banged to and fro with an agitated sound.

"*Enough!*" she cried. "That will be enough!"

Her footsteps came ringing on the boards, and I shrank back as she sailed through the door. Her anger went by me like a ship on fire: I swear I felt its heat.

The rocker on the porch soon stopped its noise. There was the dripping fog, the harbor bell; nothing else. After a while I tiptoed to the door. My father stood with his back to me, staring out at the blank night.

"Daddy?"

He turned on me. "For Christ's *sake*, Susie! What are you

doing lurking there! I told you to get to *bed!*" He had never spoken to me in such a tone in all my life, and I began to cry.

"Oh, my God!" he said. "Tears, now! *Tears!*" He left me and strode through the lounge. The old man never stirred.

My father apologized the next morning; he was really sorry and concerned. And he told me that I was not to worry about what I'd heard; that he and Mrs. Fenwick had become very fond of one another, that she had caused him pain and he'd reacted badly—"hurt her feelings," he put it—but that everything would be "all right," because he was going to explain to her and tell her he was sorry.

"Grownups aren't always as grown up as they'd like to be," he said. "Years haven't much to do with it, unfortunately. You'll find that out."

I was finding it out. And everything was not "all right" with Mrs. Fenwick. She would not see my father. She would not speak to him.

"But she'd see *you*, Susie," he said, shameless with anxiety as the morning wore on; we were to leave at noon. "You go see her, you ought to, anyway. Knock on the door and when she hears your voice . . . tell her . . . no, wait, I'll send a note with you."

With his letter in my hand I walked slowly down the stuffy hall and around the corner to her door. Number 33. I knocked on it, then called her name, but there was no answer. I tried the handle; the door was not locked and I opened it gently, planning to leave the letter on her bureau. I was curious, too. I had never seen her room.

She was lying on the bed asleep.

I stood and looked at her. She had taken the pins out of her hair; they lay in a small heap on the bedside table with her earrings and a wrinkled handkerchief. Her hair covered her shoulders in a silky fall. Her eyelashes were dark and long.

She slept gracefully, with her mouth closed, and the room was full of her perfume.

I looked at her for a minute, or a second; long enough, anyway, to remember her asleep forever, and then I went out of the room and closed the door as quietly as I could. I tore the letter up and dropped the pieces into one of the red fire buckets that hung on a hook by the stairs. Then I leaned against the wall and waited for my heart to quiet down; it was banging like the rockers on the porch.

When I turned the corner I saw my father waiting in his doorway.

"Did you give it to her, Sue? What did she say?"

"She tore it up," I said. "She never even opened it. She just stood there and tore it up."

"Oh," he said, and his face turned dull. "Well, I guess she's . . . well, never mind. Never mind . . . Are you all ready?"

Indeed I was ready, and more than ready.

"Hurry, Daddy, come on, let's go!"

"Yes, all right . . . oh, here's Calvin. These two, Calvin; I'll take the others . . ." And then as I waited, nervously snapping my hat elastic under my chin, he turned away, turned to the window, and put his hand to his forehead just for a moment as if his head ached, and something about that simple gesture showed me how unhappy he was. I was appalled. I must tell him. Could I tell him? But I thought I could not. I thought I had gone too far, and was afraid.

"Daddy, let's *go!*"

"Yes. All right. Right now."

He didn't even turn his head as we went by her door, and I was perfectly miserable all the way home. I suppose I knew then that by my action I had lost my father just as truly as Mrs. Fenwick had.

Doublefields

I know full well that I am a vintage man. A man of good vintage, too, though dangerously close to that point in time when, to draw a parallel, a first-rate champagne is threatened; when its effervescence is still intact, but who can say for sure that in the next year, or even in the next hour, it may not start to fade? One lives, therefore, on a rather poignant edge of doubt. And to pursue the metaphor (perhaps in fact the fading has begun already? To pursue metaphors instead of relinquishing them may be regarded as a first suspicious symptom) but to pursue the metaphor anyhow, one must concede that champagne is no longer to the public taste; a few appreciate it though they guzzle it, others, revering its cost, pretend to appreciate it; but in truth it does not compare in favor to the bulldozing of bourbon whisky, or to the loud bell-ringing effect of gin. However, *de gustibus*, etc. Who can change the world?

My mother was a Portious of the Baltimore Portiouses, which may account for some of my characteristics, and of course *does*. The whole family, right down to the roots of the tree, has sprouted its eccentrics. Palamon Portious, in the eighteenth century, went about in a sedan chair carried by four slave girls, all mighty handsome, and none older than sixteen. He shocked the scholars by naming his new house Tartarus Place, and died of an apoplectic stroke at thirty-six. An early Portious, crusading to Jerusalem, found the Infidel more to his taste than the True Believer, and happily embraced Islam and a seraglio. Another spent his adult life in a house constructed in a tree with a rope ladder which could be retracted at the approach of relatives. At a later date, my Portious great-aunt Dulcibella played end man in a touring minstrel show for seven years without being identified as female even by her colleagues. In my mother's case the deviant tendency was softened to occasional somnambulism, and in her later years to a very gentle and tactful kleptomania.

My father, Thornhold Fater, is responsible for the ballast in my nature, and, luckily for me, in my bank account as well. He came of a good family himself, of course (the Philadelphia Faters), but a solid one. A very solid one. My aunts, all six of them, reminded me, when they were together, of the great stones of Salisbury Plain: enduring, silent, somewhat crude by nature; and my uncles, like my father, appear in retrospect as possible offspring of a union between Zeus and Mrs. Beeton: full-bearded, robust, and, I am convinced, virtuous far beyond the demands of society.

My sister, Violet, and I were raised according to the mores of wealthy families in that halcyon period just before the onslaught of the new brute century. We grew up at the family place, Doublefields, in a house of wonderful ugliness and splendor, that crouched, goffered as a stegosaurus, in the midst of acres of imitation English park. The interior of the house, true to the esthetics of the day, was mobbed with furniture and ornaments. Servants infested it, running up and down the dark back stairs and whisking through the passages; there was always the crackle of a starched apron somewhere, the suppression of laughter behind closed doors.

As infants Violet and I each had a nurse, then a governess, and later a governess for Violet and a tutor for me. Our parents were remote unquestioned monarchs, like the higher gods of mythology. We, their children, spent our days under the rules, views, and prejudices of hired persons. Often Violet, in a lace hat that wept around the edges, and I in an Eton cap, would trundle along in the governess cart behind our coughing pony, Jeppo. It was almost the only privacy we ever had. We never considered rebellion, it did not occur to either of us that this condition of well-furnished boredom was not the universal dwelling place of childhood. Yes, and I am content that this was so! By the time I was twelve and Violet eleven we could speak French and German fluently and were well-read in Latin; we could mask our feelings like royalty, were beginning to be cognizant of the contents of the top drawer, and we had *manners*. Our manners were of the classic, stylized type that one sees no longer in this country and this time, and we had been trained in them as dancers are trained to the ballet, until they were almost entirely habitual and effortless.

Violet completed the requirements demanded of her by marrying well at the end of her first season. She was eighteen when she married the Earl of Finchcape, and I remember her on her wedding day seated at the dressing table, head in her hands, her veil about her like a shroud.

"Porty," she said. (I am named Portious for my mother's

family.) "Porty, why am I marrying that poor creamed turbot downstairs? Oh, why, oh, why, oh, why?"

She looked so desperate, as though she might be sick or throw herself from a window, that I was repelled and had to leave the room. But I have never seen her terrified since; and Finchcape proved to be a very considerate husband, rich and forgiving.

As for me, I never married. Earlier I have implied that in myself there is a trace of the Portious eccentricity, and you are perhaps wondering how this expresses itself in my case. I will tell you. I have never in my life felt passion for a human being; that is to say I have never felt love. Never a trace of the condition of the heart which like a "lark at break of day arising/From sullen earth, sings hymns at heaven's gate."

I have watched it in others with curiosity, surprise, but never, I swear, with envy.

And yet I am not invulnerable. I know, I sense, what love must be. Though it is not kindled in me by any living being, yet sometimes it is kindled.

As far as I can recall, the first clear example of this—would you say trait? gift? affliction?—of mine, took place in my twelfth year. I had formed a friendship with a boy of my own age, a very well-connected boy, named Brander Bailey; and one day, in looking over his toys and possessions (he had many), my fascinated attention was claimed, of all things, by a paperweight! I hasten to explain that it was no ordinary paperweight. Though it contained a snow scene, it was nothing like those fluid-filled spheres that, when shaken, generate an interior blizzard. It was a half-globe of crystal at the bottom of which, on the surface of an ivory disk, a snow scene was painted. It showed a view of a village square: half-timbered houses all turbaned with snow, a Gothic church, and little people busy at their purposes. Beyond the town, glimpsed at the end of a long street or lane, there was a prospect of winter woods, and beyond those a series of white, fantastic mountains like the crests of cockatoos.

Now, as I looked into this little contained world, looked deep into it, concentrated on it, something happened. I was conscious of the removal of some accepted, till now unrealized, barrier to my vision. It was as if the scene disclosed to me, invited me into, a memory that was not my own. Nonetheless a memory. Yes, I thought, or, rather, felt, *yes;* I go through the square and through the lane to the woods; and there is the old beggar woman's hut, and there *he* is, gathering faggots, the rags are tied around his legs with bands, and his breath is visible on the air as if he were breathing out his holy spirit. The flakes turn and hiss among the boughs, the cat comes picking her way through the snow, the cold bell rings in the tower . . . I am at home again.

All this, you understand, was the experience of an instant, but it was an experience.

"Brander," I said, "will you give me this?"

His reply, quite reasonably, was a laugh.

"Well, what will you take for it then?" I persisted. "I've got to have it."

"I'll take ten dollars," he said.

That was out of the question. Though we were the children of a wealthy family, we were never given money to spend, beyond a penny or a nickel from time to time. Our Christmas gold pieces were spirited away from us the moment we received them and deposited in a bank, safely out of reach.

In the end it was decided that when he next came to Doublefields Brander would make his choice among my possessions and we would effect a trade.

During the intervening days I could think of nothing but the snow sphere. I longed to own it, to look into it whenever I wished, and remember, and experience again the marvelous sense of recognition, of *homecoming*. I lost my interest in food, lay awake at night, and in short exhibited the symptoms, as I understand them, of one in love.

Brander was true to his word. When he came to Doublefields he brought the paperweight in his pocket; but he was a canny fellow and would not even let me see it till he had made his choice. And then he proved difficult.

"I don't want any of *your* stuff, Fater," he said, at the end of a long day. "What I want is downstairs in the drawing room: that little horse on the bookcase."

I tried my best to make him choose something else. The horse was a small T'ang terra cotta, with a flying saddlecloth and a raised hoof. My grandfather had picked it up in China, and it was valuable. But Brander was adamant, so in the end I smuggled it up to the schoolroom and gave it to him. The wonderful snow scene was delivered into my hands.

The house, as I have said, was almost a museum of objects, small and large. It was at least a fortnight before anyone noticed that the little horse was missing, and I had had time to lay my plans.

That year there was a new second-maid in the house, Agnes Cleary (I have never forgotten her name), whom I detested. The palpable presence of emotion has always been disagreeable to me, and Agnes was a perfect wilderness of emotion. She was an ignorant Irish girl with plum-red cheeks and large rabbity eyes. Vulnerable to a degree, she exuded an aura of animal terror mixed with prayerful hope, and when she dashed about the house doing her work, there was almost a smell of panic about her, and you could hear her breath seized in in gasps. I hated her for these reasons; so when at last the little horse was missed, I had my story ready.

"Porty, *you* hadn't been playing with it, had you, dear?" asked my mother from her chaise longue. (She spent much of her time there, as did many leisured ladies of that day: delicate health was thought to be a credit to the aristocracy.)

"No, Mama, never," I said. "But the other day I heard—I hate to say it, Mama—but I did hear a smash when Agnes was dusting in the drawing room. I asked her what had happened, and she said: 'Nothing, Master Porty, just the brush against the pan,' but she'd covered the pan with her apron, and down by the chair leg I saw a little piece of something, and it was—I *think* it was—a thing that looked like a little horse's hoof. She leaned down and grabbed it before I could—"

My mother put her finger on the bell: and not long after that, lingering behind the door, I could hear a colloquy of voices, and then a loud one bursting out, uncontrolled: "Oh, Ma'am, no, honest to God, oh, never, never! Oh, I *never!*"

I tiptoed away to the top of the house where I could not hear any more and soon, from the attic window I witnessed Agnes's departure. Crying, disheveled, she stumbled to the hired trap, and Carter, the footman, stowed her trunk on the roof without speaking to her. I do not remember what my feelings were.

It was a long time before the snow sphere lost its power for me because, instinctively, I husbanded it, not permitting myself to look into it more than once a day; and each time I was rewarded by the sense of a glad return to—what? To something I had been missing all my life.

In this connection it may well be argued that owing to the agency of the snow scene I understood for a time one aspect of the phenomenon of human love, since it was not the scene alone, but the concept of "him," whoever "he" was, that held me spellbound. It never occurred to me to question who "he" might have been; it was enough simply to relive for an instant (if that is what I did), the jubilant sense of my return to "him."

Little by little, however, the charm, as every charm must do, wore thin; and then wore out. The day came when I saw the paperweight as a toy, an ornament, and nothing more, and knew that its magic was gone forever. I gave it to Violet, who subsequently broke it in a fit of temper.

It was two years before another such experience occurred, this time on a steamer bound for France, *La Reine de Navarre*.

My tutor, Avery Giles, who was taking me to meet my parents and sister in Paris, was a dark, thin man; I suppose he was young, thirty or so, though not till now have I thought of him as young. He had a pinched crowlike face, the face of a man who is pressed by some interior concern that never gives him peace. I am certain that this look has nothing to do with facial conformation. One sees it less in the shape of the lips than in the stricture at their corners; less in the eyes than in the apprehensive cant of the eyebrows. Moreover, in such a person this look seems as much a part of the being as those eyebrows themselves, so that one cannot attribute it to some temporary pain such as loss in love (though the concern itself may often have commanded such a loss). I believe it more likely that the unremitting pressure has some prosaic cause: insomnia, or chronic constipation, or a nagging purse. In Giles's case the latter is conceivable.

The *Reine de Navarre* was an aging vessel even in that day, but she had a plushy elegance that was much to my taste. I loved to sit in the main saloon after dinner, playing cribbage, or checkers with Avery while he nursed a glass of cognac, and I sipped at green mint or *crème de cacao*, which I found as pleasing to my tongue as candy.

I loved the flash of jewels and the luster of satin. In those days women *dressed*. A background to the sparkle and chatter was the dark bossed mahogany of the walls; the great chandeliers would lean slowly to one side, slowly to the other; and when the orchestra stopped playing one could hear the constant sounds of stress and adjustment, the long racking creaks and snarls, ever present in the timbers of a moving vessel.

The orchestra was composed of four instruments: piano, violin, cello, and harp. The pianist was a young man, the cellist middle-aged, the violinist old. The harpist was the only woman. She was a hunchback and had no age. I remember how her small bony-fingered hands used to scramble over the strings like spiders mending a web.

What they played was shipboard music, saccharine, light-hearted: watered opera airs, waltzes, polkas. One waltz I still remember: *"Les Oiseaux d'Avril,"* a tune that was much in vogue just then; cheap, mournful, and as sweet to my ears as the taste of the liqueur was to my tongue. Sweet to Avery's ears, too. Whenever the orchestra played it he would whistle it softly, and I noticed as he did so that his eyes would wander from our game, and I saw to whom they wandered.

She was the young French wife of an American businessman: Mrs. Cameron. Sargent has painted many like her, he may even have painted her; Cameron was extremely successful. She had the sort of very fine white skin that nurses a greenish shadow at the inside of the elbow, in the hollows of the cheek and neck. Her hair was a live shining black, and her mouth was as red as the mouths of Sargent's women. Though I do not covet it, I can appreciate the beauty of women.

Cameron, her husband, was an open-faced usual sort. He still had all his hair, and his teeth were good; he was neither old nor bad-looking, but there was something about him that I have since seen more than once among my compatriots; something that I can only describe as *halted*. It was as though, having reached a certain point in time and endeavor, he had paused, and one felt that the pause threatened him, might become permanent; that it would thicken him in body and spirit; that, in short, if he lingered he was in danger of imprisonment.

Perhaps I imagine all this; in retrospect it is the way I see

him. But who dares trust the judgment imposed years ⸾
a memory?

My recollection of his laugh, however, I know to ⸾
curate. It was a high neighing giggle, all falsetto; sta
coming from that solid, glowing man. I can imagine that
one growing fond of him might be tempted to recons
when Cameron laughed that laugh: temporarily it made ⸾
such a fool. I remember *her* face when it happened, on
she looked down at her lap and then, only for an instar
looked up, sideways, and at Avery. I saw it.

There was another one who looked at him, covertly, and ⸾
saw this, too. It was the hunchbacked harpist with her bird
face and her frizzled bang. What was it about Avery, I have
asked myself. There were far handsomer men aboard. I suppose it was the look I have described, the look of pain or
concern, that some women might regard as a challenge, or as
a puzzle to be solved or shared. These impressions I stored
in my mind, perhaps already sensing that they might prove
useful. (I fancy I was perceptive for my age.)

Even this harpist had her little vanity; she was vain about
her slender hands. Possibly it was this which had drawn her
to her instrument in the first place: it is a perfect setting for
the hands. She further emphasized this attribute of hers by
wearing a pair of bracelets, or bangles, which were rich and
heavy, drawing attention to the delicacy of her wrists. Before
she played she always removed these bracelets, placing them
carefully in her lap, or on a little table close at hand. She never
forgot to put them on again when the music was over.

When we were but three nights from port the moon waxed
full. Already aboard ship there was that sense of excitement, of
hastening friendship and romantic pressure, which often at-
tends the final phase of a long voyage. I have observed it
many times: a little world is coming to an end; a little life

has nearly run its course. Therefore do not waste a moment of it, value it, above all experience it! The full moon only served to heighten the general exhilaration. None but the infants and the aged went willingly to bed, and the orchestra played late.

It was this reckless sense of hastened gaiety, I am sure, that caused my tutor, usually so conservative and secret, to surprise the other passengers one evening. It was late; we were as usual sitting in the main saloon, and the orchestra began to play its final number: "*Les Oiseaux d'Avril.*" But this time instead of whistling it low, as he had done before, Avery sang the words, full voice, and his voice was beautiful. The clutter of talk died away, ceased entirely, as Avery sang boldly, from his heart. I knew for whom he sang, and so did she. Her cool pale skin was warmed with color; she watched him steadily, and when the song was ended she applauded with the others, though rather moderately, I thought. Alone of the musicians, the harpist also clapped her hands, and her face, too, was flushed.

Avery would not sing again, though he was asked, and soon he was ordering me to bed, where I had no intention of remaining. When he had left me, I got up and dressed. I knew I was perfectly safe. For several nights now his berth had been unoccupied till dawn.

Nevertheless I scouted the corridors with care: nothing there but pairs of shoes put out for the steward, sidling a bit this way, then that, with the ship's listing. I heard voices, laughing, ocean through the open ports: a sound of rushing drapery.

It was very late; the top deck, when I reached it, was nearly deserted; a few couples whispering or kissing, and I avoided them. Smoke steamed back from the funnels in two great capes of darkness; deep in the vessel the engine room throbbed like a savage heart. Everything I touched had a skin of dew on

it. I tiptoed along the deck. The night was all my own. Like the chandeliers in the main saloon, the stars and moon in the sky leaned slowly to one side, slowly to the other.

And then near the prow-end of the deck, where shadow was deep between the hanging lifeboats, I came upon Mrs. Cameron and Avery in an embrace. I swear I had not meant to, emphatically had never wished to! Raw emotion, as I have said, has always repelled me—yes, even frightened me; but now I saw, whether I wished or not. Sight was frozen to my eye.

She lay in his arms as though without their support she would have fallen. The moon had turned her jet-black hair to indigo, and all her skin was tinted with blue light: cheek, neck, shoulder, and then I saw with horror—horror that returns to me even now as I write of it—that Avery had opened her bodice, and her naked breast lay under his hand. His hand kept moving over it, shaping it, stroking it, as though himself were creating it. The breast was perfect: round, upright, flawless, and under Avery's searching fingers the small dark nipple stood up like a thimble. I saw it, and the sound I made—I could not help the sound I made—caused them to spring apart, to turn, she clutching her dress together, he aghast and raging.

"In God's name, what are you doing!"

But I heard no more; I fled, down one companionway and then another, along the deck and into the main saloon. No one was there but an elderly gentleman, drunk and snoring, his jowl spread out on his buckled shirt front.

The piano was closed but the harp was still uncovered. That was unusual, and I noted it from my distant vantage point of shock. And something glittered on the nearby table: for the first time the harpist had forgotten her bracelets. I went over and picked them up.

Without thinking, as I stood there looking at the bracelets,

I brushed the fingers of my other hand across the harp strings. I brushed my fingers across the harp strings. . . .

And with the sound, shock ebbed from all my being, for there was the rain again. There *is* the rain, I thought. . . . The rain that is our shelter, our ally; it sings to us and mothers us, so that we in our polished shell—my love and I—think of our childhood for a moment. . . .

Yes, there I was, a child myself, a lad not yet fourteen, but for the brief duration of this experience I was a grown man remembering far childhood; a man in love, a man at home. And so profound was my contentment that I longed never to outlive the moment, and brushed my fingers across the harp again.

"In God's name, what are you doing!" demanded the roused drunk gentleman, his words and rage identical to Avery's.

I took my leave, the harpist's bracelets chinking in my pocket.

And Avery really made it very easy for me. He was waiting in the cabin when I came down.

"All right, you little monster, what's your price?" he said.

"The harp," I answered promptly.

"The *what?*"

"The harp in the main saloon. The orchestra's harp."

"Are you crazy, suddenly?"

"No," I said. "It's just that that's my price, and you can get it for me. Otherwise I'll tell. I won't wait to tell Papa and Mama, either. I'll tell Mr. Cameron."

"Now look here a minute, listen to reason," Avery pleaded, and offered me alternatives, every one of which I rejected. The only thing on earth I wanted was the harp.

"*How* can I get it for you? Why should she give it up?"

"Tell her you'll buy her a better one in Paris . . . or pay

her for it now. But I don't think you'll have to. I've seen the way she watches you."

Something, the tiniest flicker of expression, told me that he had seen this, too.

"But she earns her living with the thing. You can't have it till we dock."

"Only two more days," I said. "And look, here are her bracelets; she forgot them tonight. You can take them to her, knock on her door, tell her . . ."

"At this hour of the night?"

"She'll let you in," I said.

"You *are* a monster," Avery said. "It would be better for the world if I had the courage to kill you."

"But you haven't the courage," I said. "So go along, now. Go along. Here are the bracelets."

That night he never returned at all, and the next evening the harpist was reported to be ill. Her instrument stood hooded on its golden foot, and the other members of the ensemble played trios.

I noticed that Mrs. Cameron sat in silence with her husband, and when she glanced in Avery's direction it was coldly, and at a point above his head.

Avery and I were just as silent; he would not speak to me at all. I could feel his loathing, a dark live thing beside me. But it did not matter. It never matters.

That was our last night out of port. Much later, sometime in the small hours, the little harpist pulled a box to the ship's rail, scrambled over it and dropped into the sea. Poor creature. In her cabin they found a note, stating that she was leaving her harp "to M. Avery Giles, the young man who sang so beautifully on Friday night."

When my father met us at the pier, he was astonished and much put out to find a full-sized harp among the luggage; but he did his best to rally.

"Well, good, well, good," he said. "But somehow, Porty, it doesn't seem a very *masculine* instrument, does it?"

I had disappointed him in many ways already.

As for Avery, having given me into my father's safekeeping, as soon as he was free of Customs he announced curtly that he was leaving my father's service as of that moment.

"But what on earth? But why?"

"I prefer not to say, sir," replied Avery, with a furious glance at me. Then he bowed to my father, turned, and was blotted away in the crowd.

"He prefers not to say for a very good reason, Papa," I explained. "Because it has something to do with a lady, you see. That lady over there," I said, nodding toward Mrs. Cameron, as she went by us with her husband. "I saw her with Avery on the top deck night before last. I can't—I don't think I *should* tell you what they were doing, Papa."

"No, don't! Don't!" my father said hastily, staring at Mrs. Cameron in profile: at the dark lashes and hair, pearl earring, sable collar, plumed hat. Youth, wealth, beauty, all at once; and as if that were not enough, sin added.

"Great Scott," said my father, stunned, and sounding almost wistful. He blew out his breath in a sort of astonished sigh.

"Well, come along, Porty. But I wish you'd waited till you go to Heaven to take up playing the harp."

Of course I never learned to play it. I did not need to. It stood in my hotel room until we left for Lugano, and by that time its magic had worn out. But how many times, until then, had a casual glissando restored to me the sound of the rain, the sight of a muted, golden room, the sense of peace and desire fused, and my love's hand in mine.

I never saw her face. I never saw any of their faces clear. I saw their figures, sometimes heard their voices, shared perfect moments of companionship with them. Yet though I knew each one of them by something which had lived far longer than my heart, I never really saw their faces clear.

When I was twenty, still in college, it was an hourglass; a large old one that stood on the window sill of a fishmonger's shop. Even by looking at it through the pane I knew that this would have a magic for me and my heart began to hurry.

I went into the strong-smelling shop, with its rows of staring mackerel and cod, its beds of ice where lobsters slowly scrambled. An old woman sat in a doorway beyond the counter, a cave of dark behind her. Her son or grandson was the clerk. I ordered a pint of oysters, then strolled to the window, took the hourglass and turned it upside down. As I watched the narrow waterfall of sand descending, it happened. It happened again: the thing which I must always write of in the present tense.

All at once it is another day, another land: three o'clock in the afternoon. Three o'clock. That least sympathetic of diurnal hours, when one is stranded on the lag of day, beached high and dry as any mackerel, on reality. And yet it is three o'clock in this place, and every wish comes true. A wind is blowing: a sunny wind that whips the grass, coarse varnished grass, that shows me we are near the sea.

The house before me is white and square with dark-green blinds: a plain house, bare of vines or trees. . . . The door is opening, I see it opening, and a woman in a white dress stands on the threshold holding a small child by the hand. I have been homesick, *homesick* for this place, and now I am returned, and all that was ill is well again; is healed again.

"How much for this?" I asked the clerk, and the old woman spoke from her cave.

" 'Tisn't for sale at all," she said. "It was me father's. He brought it with him from the other side. It's all that's left of him; all that was saved when his house burned down and him inside it. . . ."

"I'll give you ten dollars for it," I said to the clerk, ignoring her. "Here, I'll give you twenty."

His mouth hung open, and the old woman rattled to her feet and tried to prevent him from taking the bills that I held out. He took them, though, oh yes, he took them; and I departed with the glass, leaving the oysters behind me in my haste.

I realized fully, now, that it was to be my lot, my destiny, that through the agency of irrelevant objects I was to be shown, from time to time, that my true lives were all about me in the false one I was living; but shown to me obliquely, with refracted brilliance; shown to me briefly, but in that brief space what hunger was appeased, what absolute joy was granted! And if it lasted for moments only, still they were the moments when I was where I belonged, and where I longed to be.

I cannot explain this and I never discussed it with anyone. To discuss might be to dispel. I only knew that these brilliant glimpses, fortuitously offered, were to be for me what mistress, marriage, wife, and children are to other men. These I had instead of family warmth and the close ties of friendship.

Oh, of course I had *friends*. The young people with whom I hunted, swam, played tennis, bridge. As a single man (and not, I confess, an ill-favored one) I was much in demand for parties and weekends in Newport, Narragansett, Saratoga. I traveled a great deal; I knew the right people. But real friends, no. No real friends.

One strange thing. As time wore on it began to be evident to me—regrettably evident—that after each of these episodes another person came to grief, often without my even having had a hand in it—knowingly. In the case of Agnes Cleary, I, of course, brought it about on purpose. In the case of the harp, though I had supposed Giles would experience discomfort, I could not have guessed the harpist's drive to suicide; and now after possessing the hourglass I learned that the old woman's anger and distress had been too much for her; had felled her like a withered tree. The young clerk told me that, bursting from his shop as I passed by, to revile me.

"It was your fault grabbing up the glass like that, and tempting me with money!" he shouted.

"You took it fairly eagerly," I remarked, and he said: "You didn't ought to have tempted me. . . ."

"I'll tell you what I'll do," I offered. "When I'm through with the hourglass—in a few weeks—I'll return it to you. And moreover you may keep the money."

"That won't bring *her* back," he said, tears actually in his eyes. "And I don't want your dirty dollars."

He threw them, crumpled, on the ground. I stepped over them and walked away. I have no doubt he picked them up again.

Luckily for me, as I have, I think, indicated, I have never wasted my substance on the barren exercise of pity, even for myself. This is no discipline that I can claim; I simply am not burdened with the emotion—presumably it is a concomitant of love. I dislike seeing animals mistreated; I have a respect for justice, and, as I hold to be the duty of those who are privileged, I contribute generously to causes for the relief of suffering. But pity? The hand put out to touch the shoulder of one in grief? (Done sometimes, but done with chill revulsion.) And tears because of someone else's tears? No, never.

So it became evident to me, and uncanny, that trouble for another invariably accompanied my acquisition of each treasure. One early morning in New York, passing what would now be called a thrift shop, I stopped abruptly, my eye seized once more by that which was magical for me alone.

In the window among the trash (a dusty lute, jardinieres, a Spanish shawl) there was a small painting, propped against an andiron. It had no frame; the varnish had darkened. I knew that it was very old and very good; but if it had been painted on china by someone's maiden aunt it would have been the same to me, since it could work the miracle.

Trees, hunters in the distance, a pair of shivering whippets. It is fall and cold. Beech leaves are scattered on the ground, pink and curled, like copper shavings. Something has sounded in the air—a bell? a horn? a voice?—it is only an echo at this instant. There is a scent of sweet decay, the smell of fall; of smoke, too; and I know that beyond the wood, beyond the hill, the great stone house is waiting, fires and candles lighting up the rooms. For a minute, a few minutes, I am back where I belong.

> Most true it is that I have looked on truth
> Askance and strangely . . .

How can I express the distillation of my joy at each view, at each return? Nothing in ordinary life compares to it except, faintly, the warmth and exquisite relief one feels in the moment, just on waking, a little before waking, when one realizes that the nightmare was a nightmare, nothing more, and all is well. *That* is the feeling, but intensified a thousandfold.

I waited for the shop to open; strolled in, examined this and that, and bought the picture for thirty dollars. I paid for it in cash and took it home under my arm. One might say, facetiously, that I took *home* home under my arm since that is what it was to me for brief yet timeless minutes till the spell wore out.

Ah, but the sad proprietor!

Hot on my heels, it seems, a dealer came into the shop to buy the picture. He had seen it the night before on his way home from the opera, and even by the light of the street lamp, he knew at once what it was: an early Verheyden, stolen years before from a London town house. He could hardly contain himself in his eagerness to get his hands on it. When he was told that it was gone, he was close to tears. He was so frantic that he told the proprietor the truth—there was no point in haggling—and offered him ten thousand dollars if he could get it back.

What could the poor shop owner do? I had paid in cash; I had left no name; he had a heart attack from sheer frustration, and never was the same again.

I heard about all this a great deal later; much too late to make amends, and by that time the picture was safely housed in a museum.

And so it happened every time: trouble for someone. There was the box of granadilla wood, for instance. That night, the very night of the sale, the former owner's wife helped herself to the cash I'd paid and eloped with his best friend.

There was the music box that twirled a pair of dancers. Grossly overpaid, the former owner celebrated by getting drunk, missed a turning on his stairs, fell down and broke his neck.

Sometimes the result was a more subtle villainy. The donor of the antique chessboard that I craved almost at once developed an irrational fear of any height above ground level, and was for the rest of his life confined to living in the basement of his splendid house. The beauty who let me have her spangled fan that evening saw her first wrinkles in her mirror, smashed the mirror against the wall, and never mingled in society again. And there was the jolly musician, from whom I bought a fiddle, and who, seldom sad before, became the victim of a steady melancholy that bleached the color from his hopes and from his ruddy face.

I could not help these things; and how could I be sure that

they were consequences? That they were not—most of them —coincidences?

And yet invariably they occurred.

But life was life, an ordinary thing three-quarters of the time: the eating and digesting, the arguing and yawning, the scratching at itches, the filling of teeth, the attending to business and to bills—the being bored and bored, and the escaping. The constant escaping.

For I was a slippery fish. I had to be. I was more than wealthy, and, as I have admitted, not ill-favored. There were those who said I was handsome out of the ordinary; and being a bachelor, I was young for a long time.

Practice made me wary and wise. There was a certain look I came to know and flee from: a speculative, questing glance that underlay flirtation, a sort of pause apparent beneath words. No gorgon's eye could chill me colder, or appall me more.

Pretty girls, so many of them: dashing, spirited, gentle, or shy. I had no wish to hurt them, but I hurt them badly, more than one. I had nothing to give them; nothing to give of humanity to any human being.

Oh, it was awkward, and sometimes it was worse. The night at the house party at Woodfen, for example, when Gates Bendle's wife came stealing to my room. I woke to see her in her nightdress, blond as Sieglinde, with her long hair hanging. I watched, paralyzed, as she crept across the rug of moonlight on her bare feet, crept to my bedside, reached out her hand . . . and I—I sprang away as if an adder touched me, and heard my stifled scream.

"Get away!" I whispered. "Get away, don't touch me!"

I see her still: frozen, hand to her mouth. I hear her whimper as she turns and runs away on her bare feet, brutally rebuffed. Rebuffed for the first time, I'll wager; she was a beauty indeed, of most accommodating morals. I felt no remorse, nothing but the cold disgust; yes, as if an adder had touched me.

I waited for the rumors to commence. I was too young to know I need not worry: no woman tells this sort of tale about herself.

There were other situations of the kind; but I soon learned to parry and evade.

And yet there came a time *when* for a time I could do neither; when, because of my unique ability (or curse), I had to play the wooer, in this case hurting a harmless individual directly.

Her name was Dolly Delavant. She was a charming-looking girl, brunette, slender. She put me in mind, a little, of Avery's Mrs. Cameron, whom I wished never to remember. Still, she was more than usually attractive and lively, rode well, read well, played bridge well, and was a beautiful dancer. (It's odd when you think of it that I should have enjoyed dancing, since it demands the clasping of a partner; yet I did enjoy it, was surpassingly good at it, and must have danced the world around at balls.)

I first met her at a Christmas house party given by my cousin Cosimo and his wife, Ethel. Dolly was well chaperoned, of course; safe to flirt with but guarded from the consequences, conditions which suited me exactly. She loved to chaff and had a nimble wit, and evidently she liked me. I was her requested escort on many an occasion, and in June she invited me, with a number of other young people, to her family's house in Newport.

The first evening there was a ball at the Duquesnes, and it was there that I first met Dolly's mother. (She had recently returned from Europe; all the time that I had known Dolly she had been under the wing of her aunt.)

Mrs. Delavant, seated in a chair, remains seated in my memory just as she was that night: a short, stout woman dressed in black and jet, with a bosom of anthracite and the eyes of a Chinese overlord. She sat in her armchair holding a small fan; not smiling—she never smiled. They said her maid touched up her hair with shoe black; they said her square white face had been "enameled." Nothing about her moved except her narrow lips, her eyes, her fan. She sat immobile in her cruel carapace of corsetings, her feet crossed unmoving in their mercilessly tiny shoes. She could not have moved, pinioned by her clothing as she was.

"Fater. Philadelphia," she told me. "I knew your uncle Ambrose."

Her voice was a surprise: though her diction was cultivated, the voice itself was gravelly and harsh like that of an inveterate cigar smoker.

"Ambrose Fater," she said. "Good stable. Good dogs."

Evidently she approved; my uncle's animals were to my credit, and more than once that night I saw her jetty eyes surveying me.

"Isn't Mama terrible?" Dolly said, as we danced. "I can't wait to get married and be free of her. . . ."

Then she blushed. I saw the tide of color sweep up across her face because of what she'd said, and I knew at once that her liking for me had turned to something warmer. I blushed, too, wretchedly embarrassed; and all in that second between one step and the next I planned to cut my visit short.

But predilection trapped me on the very next day.

I had seen Dolly's little watch a hundred times, pinned to her dress by a fleur-de-lis of pearls. Now for some reason she had unfastened it and left it on a table in the drawing room. I was alone there. The summer wind filled out the curtains gently and there was a muted clatter from the kitchen. I was hungry, and catching sight of Dolly's watch I picked it up idly and opened it to see the time.

How can it be that a watch, a woman's watch, with its fussy little decorated face, its tiny bustling of sound, can give me the enormous vision of a sea? A sea—a harbor—that is calm and blinding, lighted up with morning. Who has laughed? The friend who sets my heart at rest with laughter. We walk along the shore together breathing the smell of clam water and roses. The waves unfold and shrink away—unfold again. The day is long and summer is long and life is long ahead of us. Cares that troubled me a moment since are gone and gone. . . .

"Why, Porty, what's so funny about my watch?"

Dolly and Randall Howe, carrying rackets, had come in through the French window. I realized that I must have been grinning like an ape.

"Let us in on the joke," drawled Randall, a prince of stuffed shirts.

"There is no joke," I said. "Dolly's little watch gave me pleasant thoughts about her. That is all."

As I put it in her hand she blushed again, happy, disconcerted. I knew that I would soon possess the watch.

But it cost me something, I can tell you! I played the part, I fancy, very well. I had seen others play it often enough; the significant glance, the gentle raillery, the hand caught surreptitiously, the compliments—this much I was prepared to give, was *able* to give. In those days it wasn't hard to play at love; a young girl's virtue was not only her prize but in my case it was a safeguard, an ally. But even so the game was difficult, abhorrent to me. Poor Dolly—for her, hope gave the lie to intuition. She sparkled, and before one's eyes her prettiness turned into beauty.

I hated the thing that I was doing, but my passion forced me to it. Why didn't I simply take the watch, steal it, let some other wretched servant take the blame? I don't know. I've asked myself a hundred times, but I could not do it.

I was to leave on a Sunday evening. After dinner I strolled with Dolly in the garden. It was dark. To this day the smell of honeysuckle bothers me; the summer house was covered with it. The sky was heavy and starless. There was no wind. I could hear my own heart beating; and then resolved but trembling I forced myself to clasp Dolly's waist; after all, I had clasped it many times in dancing . . . but this was different, terrifying. I forced myself to clasp her waist, to stroke her arm. I pressed my cheek to hers and then my lips, and she—I could feel it in her—yielded, leaned against me, bemused, expecting more. She turned her face so that her mouth was under mine. Her fingers searched beneath my jacket, found my heart.

"How fast it goes; a little hammer beating out a message—"

" 'Lovely Dolly,' it is saying. 'Lovely Dolly Delavant.' "

"Lovely, only, and not love?"

"Love, too. Love, too, of course," I lied, cold as ice and, worse, revolted, but she didn't guess. My shaking voice shook for another reason, so she thought.

The stable bell rang out the hour.

I drew away. "Oh, God, I'll have to leave in a moment."

"Not now, oh, Porty, *not* just now. I've waited . . . yes, I have, I've waited a long time. . . ." She held me closely and I held her, too, poor girl, hating it, *hating* it!

"Dolly, I must go . . . my boat."

"There'll be another in the morning."

"I have a meeting in the morning. Ten o'clock."

She drew away a little, trying to inspect me in the dark. I laughed gently and pulled her back to me; close to my outraged, humiliated heart.

"Lovely Dolly," I repeated. "Give me a keepsake till we meet again."

She laughed, too, reassured perhaps.

"What shall I give you, then?"

"Maybe your little watch? The one that made me smile, thinking of you?"

She unclasped it slowly from the bodice of her dress, languidly, as if this were the first motion to divest herself of . . . everything, of all she wore.

"And what will you give me in return?" she asked, smiling lazily, warmly.

I had thought of this, and now unfastened a charm that hung from my own watch chain: a carnelian intaglio set in gold on which the words "Forget thee? Never!" had been engraved—the property once of a fat Fater uncle who in youth, presumably, had ignited a transient spark in someone's bosom. I pressed it to my lips and gave it to Dolly, feeling like the knave and fool I was, but the small watch, still warm, was safely in my hand.

"I'll keep it all my life," she said.

Then I did embrace her again, with all the ardor of my eagerness to be away, with the grateful relief that soon this would be over. The blessed stable bell rang out the quarter.

"Now I must really go," I said.

"No, Porty, not yet. Stay! Stay . . ."

"How I wish I could. . . ."

"When will I see you, then?"

"Soon," I babbled, helplessly. "Very soon, dear. Really."

Again she drew away, trying to inspect my face.

" 'Soon' is a silly, feeble word. *When?*" she demanded. "Not 'soon.' *When?*"

"On the weekend," I replied, retreating. "On Friday afternoon."

"Do you promise?" Doubt was starting in her, after all. "Porty, do you?" She ran to me, seized my hand, pressed it and tried to hold it.

"Of course I promise," I told her, kissed her quickly and fled. Fled is the word.

But when Friday came I was on the high seas, on my way to visit Violet in England.

Before I sailed, however, I went to Tiffany's and bought

the prettiest little watch they had—an exquisite thing of diamonds and enamel—and had them send it to her; without a note, of course. There was not anything to say.

Her letters reached me finally; first bewildered, then incredulous, then despairing. She was very young, after all, and had not learned to mask her feelings. Yet she had control and pride: there were only four letters, each written within a week of the other, and then there was silence. Two months later, when I returned to Doublefields, I found a package waiting for me. In it were the small Tiffany watch and the charm. There was no note, yet I felt that Dolly had somehow had the last word. The intaglio, taken from the box had a baleful glow in the afternoon sunlight, and its sentimental phrase seemed ominous, prophetic: "Forget thee? Never!"

That summer of my trip to England was the summer of the fateful August. Who never lived through it cannot imagine what that time was like in England, and only those who lived through it and what followed can conceive of its eternal luster in the memory. Fair day followed on fair day, shining on the young, the beautiful, the gifted, the romantic. All, in one's recollection, bathed in an endless afternoon: in a time of play, of tennis parties, teas, regattas, dances, and all the players living in youth's undoubting sense of immortality; living more strongly in it, maybe, than any other generation. Or does one only think so thinking of it afterward?

Strange, how long that summer seems in memory; yet it was short, cut off forever on the third of August. Rupert Brooke lifted his radiant head and went to battle, and others as radiant, perhaps, but lacking the music, joined in and followed to the slaughter.

I was fortunate, since my passage on the *Adriatic* was automatically canceled, in being able to band with a group of other Americans and charter a South American sugar boat. It

took us three weeks to make the crossing, the vessel stank of
fermented cane, and the storms were heavy, though not so
heavy as the one we'd fled from.

But of course a young man could not flee forever. Not wishing to be drafted, I enlisted in the navy in the spring of nine-
teen-seventeen. Strings, mercifully, were pulled for me. Mercifully and essentially. Faced with bloodshed and heroics, with
human drama, tragedy, and terror, what would I have become?
A nattering wreck, a jelly, a lunatic! I do not count myself a
coward in the usual sense; the physical danger, noise, suspense,
and filth of battle would not frighten me. It is the results of
these things, the responses in others, the fears and rages they
might feel—I cannot bear them; I should be a jelly. So strings
were pulled, though not for the true reason—but because my
father would not have his only son endangered. (What would
have happened to me had I not been rich, and my people
selfish and influential?)

So mine, for the most part, was a merry war. As an ensign
assigned to a patrol boat, the *Jack Rose* (it had been my
uncle's cruiser and I knew it well), I was stationed in Newport,
which suited me above all things. I knew the people who
counted. My uniforms were well tailored, and I was a thor-
oughly eligible extra man at a time when men not in their
dotage were scarce.

I suppose it was inevitable in that setting that I should run
into Dolly Delavant again. But Delavant no longer: she, who
was rich, had married riches and gone to live in Cleveland;
sometimes, though, she returned to visit her mother and aunt
and we would meet at parties. She spoke to me, of course, but
barely; it was all I deserved, and it bothered me not at all. I
could see from my detached outpost that she was more beautiful than she had been: a little heavier, perhaps, and less artless.
Both these changes were becoming.

But I had not bargained—nor had she—on the possibility

that we might find ourselves sharing a roof again. So it was, however: a weekend in Narragansett at the house of a young couple named Joiner—Philip and Cassandra Joiner. There were others, eight in all, which was fortunate. We seldom found ourselves alone together, but when we did Dolly always turned her back and walked away. Poor girl, if she had known how little it mattered . . .

The Joiners' house was rich and rather beautiful. I remember yellow rooms, roses, mirrors, too many photographs in silver frames, a head of Cassandra done by Despiau. In the mirror above the drawing-room mantel the girandoles were married to their own reflections, doubling their lusters. And there between them, on a crystal pedestal, I found my magic: a Tanagra figure, seated, swathed in drapery, hand beneath her thoughtful chin. The head was the typical classic head, broad brow, straight nose, curled hair and chignon, tinged, still, with polychrome. Even before I touched her (for always I must touch and hold the agents of my magic) I knew that she would work the spell.

My hands were shaking as I lifted her down.

And there is the acrid smell of thyme and tansy: the buzzing field. It is noon. The day has stopped, is stalled, as it is sometimes, on noon itself; pinned to the brilliance and stillness of the zenith. The insects' noise, the distant quaverings of goats are part of the stillness. High in the air a bird lies motionless on light, and in the bleached grass my friend lies sleeping. Oh, God, oh, God: it is a second of utter peace that lasts forever.

"Porty, are you seeing ghosts, or is she talking to you, or what?" Cassandra said, laughing at me; and in the mirror I saw Dolly look up sharply, watching as I replaced the figure.

"What an exquisite thing," I said. "Really, though, it should be in a museum."

"We think that's where it came from." Cassandra laughed again. (She was one of those irritating women who use laughter as punctuation.) "The legend is that Phil's great-uncle Charlie stole it from a museum in Athens." (Laugh.) "It was to win a bet, they say. He was always doing crazy things, and died of a broken neck at thirty-five when he tried to tightrope-walk the ridgepole of the house." (Laugh.) "At three in the morning." (Laugh.) "With a champagne glass in one hand and a bottle in the other." (Laugh.) "I must say we've always felt a little guilty about that figure. . . ."

"You should, you know. She ought to be in a museum," I said severely. "As a matter of fact, I know a member of the board of directors at the Metropolitan, a friend of Father's. . . . Perhaps I could . . ." Perhaps I could get my hands on it, I thought; keep it as long as it was of use to me, and then turn it over to him.

"Good heavens, no!" Cassandra cried. "Think of the statute of limitations, after all. It was Phil's great-uncle, remember. In eighteen eighty-*two*, or something." (Laugh.) "It wasn't us. Goodness, no, Porty, we love her!"

I loved her, too, God knows, and would have to figure out a way to have her. So far, I had never failed.

The weather was bad on Saturday and we stayed indoors all day, playing bridge. More than once I caught myself looking longingly at the small statue on the mantel, and more than once I saw that Dolly's eyes observed me.

On Sunday the bright sun came out. We swam, played tennis. I was due in Newport that evening; time was growing short, and I had not yet developed a reasonable strategy. While the others were taking tea on the terrace late in the afternoon, I strolled into the drawing room again to the mantel. My face in the mirror shocked me: a concentrated, mercenary face, almost fanatical; and again I saw how my hand shook as I reached for the figure.

"You want it, don't you, Porty?" said Dolly suddenly. I had not heard her come in, or seen her in the mirror; she had stayed beyond its range. "You want it very badly, don't you?"

Lightly she plucked the little figure from beneath my hand.

"You are unscrupulous when you want *things*, aren't you? I wonder you don't steal them instead of using other people's feelings, decency, kindness, love, as instruments to get them. To get your silly *things*. Because that's what you do, isn't it, Porty?"

I was appalled at her astuteness; no one else had come so close to guessing. And yet, of course, she had not really guessed at all. She held the figure in her hands, turning it lightly, carelessly, hardly looking at it, looking at me. My heart was in my throat; and since it was there it interfered with my voice.

"What nonsense," I said hoarsely, almost croaking, and reached my hand out for the figure. "What nonsense. It's only that it's such a lovely thing—"

"*Was* a lovely thing, you mean," Dolly said, stepping away, and she lifted the figurine and dashed it to the hearth, where it shattered into fragments, almost into dust.

As I stared at her unbelievingly I saw her mother in her for a moment: that hard, burned, beady woman, hating life. For just a second she confronted me like that, and then she cried in a loud voice: "Oh, Porty, how careless of you! It must have been priceless. Oh, Cassandra," she hurried to the door calling. "See what poor Porty has done!"

I knew that I'd let Dolly have her story; I owed it to her in a way. But as I knelt down to gather up the pieces I was as deprived as she had ever been by my rejection. If revenge is sweet then she had tasted nectar. But I doubt it is a taste that lingers on the tongue.

Our parents died within a year of one another in the early twenties. Violet and I inherited Doublefields, though neither of us lived there any longer, and after the crash of twenty-nine we decided to sell it. Not that we were in need, by any means, but we felt the place was far too large and difficult to staff when we were constantly away. In the end it was purchased (at an excellent price) and converted into a home for wealthy mental cases.

And life went on; eventually through another war, and then another. My bridge became expert, my tennis slower. I found my amulets in many lands and sometimes they were odd indeed: a child's toy engine in Berlin, a brass door knocker in Cornwall, a furled umbrella in the Garrick Club (I did steal that one). I found them, used them—or they used me—and when the magic was worn out I hastened to be rid of them. I could not bear them any more.

And then, for years, I collected what I liked as other people do, because the objects appealed to reason and to taste; not because I was obsessed. For me, as for others, passion's season was drawing to a close.

I had determined, late in the nineteen-fifties, to pay a visit to my sister and her husband. Finchcape had been seriously ill; I felt that his time was growing short, and booked passage in August on the *Queen Elizabeth*. (I never fly.)

Lodestar, Finchcape's place in Cumberland, couchant on slopes of velvet, trees grouped at a respectful distance, was always an impressive sight, washed smooth and clean by all its centuries of rain. It was raining that day, too, of course: the northern English rain, unassertive but relentless, that persuades mosses to take root on stone, that dims the lakes, and lights the fires of green in lawns like those of Lodestar.

Panfish, the butler (God bless the English for their names), and four spaniels received me at the door. Courteous and fleet, the perfect manservant, he led me through the large hall (shooting sticks, umbrellas, gum boots, mackintoshes, a ceiling by Angelica Kauffmann, dog baskets, damask curtains— eighteenth-century, priceless, darned with cobwebs), through the drawing rooms to the orangery, where my sister and her husband were waiting.

Violet stood up to greet me, and I suffered her to kiss my cheek, the dry, brief kiss of a relative. Endurable.

I had not seen her in seven years, and in that time the transformation had taken place: the last reminders of youth that had lingered so long in her appearance were gone, and she was old. Her dyed hair was frayed and lifeless and her eyes looked weary in their nests of wrinkles.

In the cold light of the orangery she saw me studying her and begged me to stop.

"You may look at me, Porty, as you must in the normal course of things," she said. "But please do not *scrutinize* me! After forty, one should be seen only in an accommodating light; after fifty, only in quick sidelong glances; after sixty—well, they should invent something to wear instead of a face; and after seventy—not seen at all!"

Violet has no malice in her nature; or very little. It would have been quite natural and justified for her to give me look for look; I am as changed as she, and a year older. But she did not.

As for Finchcape, poor fellow, he was confined to a wheelchair. The light was not kind to him, either; to none of us. But of course, we lied.

"You're looking remarkably fit," I said, as I took his hand.

"And you've not aged a day in twenty years," he returned.

The rain dinned musically on the roof. Beyond the glass walls, one saw the stone urns and finials of the terrace, sodden roses flayed amongst the balusters—beyond these, greens diminishing to green. . . .

We talked. We told each other what we wished of what had happened during recent years. It was pleasant, yet melancholy, too, to be together, now, when once we had been together young.

"Hard to adjust oneself to change. Wretched," Finchcape (whose nickname was Toppy) remarked at one point. As he spoke he lifted his hand, wearily, to his forehead. I noticed he was wearing a signet ring I'd never seen before.

I felt something . . . an intimation. . . .

"A handsome ring, that, Toppy," I observed.

He looked at it. "Yes. It belonged to my great-great-uncle Barts. Peregrine, he was. Peregrine Octavius. Seventeenth century. Bossle Hall and all that—"

"Spelled Bostwhistle, pronounced Bossle," Violet interjected. "A handsome devil; at least in his peruke. They all were. I often wonder how they looked when they took them off and hung them on the bedpost?"

"Bald as buzzards, probably," her husband said. "Most of them. Plucked. Reduced. Of course they *had* to take them off, I mean, didn't they? Imagine them at love in bed! Those curly portieres clapping on their shoulders! Stifling, I mean to say. For both of them. Distracting, too."

"Possibly ticklesome, as well," Violet surmised. Finchcape gave an old man's snicker, and then, perhaps because of my expression, he changed the subject.

"Look at it, Porty. It was given him by his mistress, a horse-eyed beauty named Zenaida Grale; she had it carved for him especially. Rather lovely, isn't it?"

He held out his hand; I took it gingerly, examining the signet: emerald intaglio, set in heavy gold.

But I did not see the carving for what it made me see. . . .

Early joy. There is the hand I must reach up to hold; the voice that laughs and loves me from above. At my side, skirts shuffle their silks together. . . . This is a day of green and yellow. Because I walk so close to them the buttercups are tall, and all the air is spangled and faceted with bird notes; sparked and stippled with spring noises. The hand takes mine, the smooth hand in which mine is lost, in which mine feels a warm enclosing palm, the clasp of total safety. . . . I shall not be lost again. . . .

"Give it to me!" I heard my own voice shouting; shouting brutally. "Give it to me, Toppy, I need it. I must have it!"

For the first time in my life I was unable to wait—or scheme —to purchase or possess.

Finchcape drew back in his chair, covering the ring with his hand.

"I say, old man, easy, for God's sake—"

But I could not and would not wait. Time was short.

"Give it to me!" I demanded, and seeing him cower in his chair I descended on him, seized his hand and worked to wrench the ring from his finger. I heard him cry out in pain, and Violet screaming: "Porty! Stop it! What's happened to you? What are you *doing?*"

Now I had the ring, and Finchcape, staring, nursed his bleeding hand. His face looked shriveled and appalled.

My sister snatched my arm.

"Porty, good God—how *could* you? What have you become?"

I shook her off, gave her a push that nearly knocked her over, and ran through the drawing room and great hall, while the dogs barked.

Young as eighteen, I raced up the stairs to my room, locked the door and leaned against it waiting for my heart to stop its clamor. "Down old heart," I said to it. "We have no time."

When it had quieted, and before the footsteps started on the stairs, I held the ring to my eyes, looked into it, and waited.

Nothing happened.

Nothing. Nothing. Nothing. Nothing.

The stone was stone only, indifferent, a traitor. The ecstasy of comprehension, of joy returned, love relived, glory lighted, the matchless sanctuary of a heart fulfilled—all were gone, would never come again. I knew it, and knowing it realized that this was my first death; for I am one of those who must die two.

When they pounded on the door I let them in. What use to keep them out?

They have given me my old room at Doublefields; my boy-hood room at the southwest corner of the house. They were kind to do that, I think. I have my things about me; all my books, the best of my collections. (Though not those objects that were the agents of my truest life, not one of those, for always, as I have said, when the spell wore out I hastened to be rid of them.)

The room is spacious; light and well proportioned. My desk is by the window facing west. I sit there when I am working on my essays. I sit there when I read.

Often, as I lift my eyes and look from that window at the domed lindens and fat lawns, I feel that I am on the verge, the not impossible verge, of seeing Jeppo, the old pony, com-ing down the drive through the zebra shadows of afternoon, and behind him the governess cart with its two passengers: Violet in her hat of weeping lace, and the rose-cheeked boy that was myself with all his life before him.